RBT Credential Workbook

TrainABA Supervision Curriculum: Volume 3

Benjamin Theisen
Zachary Bird

RBT Credential Workbook
TrainABA Supervision Curriculum: Volume 3

Benjamin Theisen & Zachary Bird
Copyright©2015

ISBN13: 978-0-9856329-7-7
3 4 5 6 7 8 20 19 18 17 16

Bx Dynamic Press
SAN: 990-1396
5031 Fair Ave #424, N. Hollywood, CA 91601

RBT Credential Workbook

TrainABA Supervision Curriculum: Volume 3

By Benjamin Theisen and Zachary Bird

TABLE OF CONTENTS

RBT™ Task List

A. Measurement

B. Assessment

C. Skill Acquisition

D. Behavior Reduction

D-01 Identify the essential components of a written behavior reduction plan. | 7 | *108*

D-02 Describe common functions of behavior | 1 | *16*

D-03 Implement interventions based on modification of antecedents such as motivating/establishing operations and discriminative stimuli. | 7 | *112*

D-04 Implement differential reinforcement procedures (e.g., DRA, DRO). | 7 | *116*

D-05 Implement extinction procedures. | 7 | *120*

D-06 Implement crisis/emergency procedures according to protocol. | 8 | *128*

E. Documentation and Reporting

E-01 Report other variables that might affect the client (e.g., illness, relocation, medication). | 8 | *132*

E-02 Generate objective session notes by describing what occurred during sessions. | 8 | *136*

E-03 Effectively communicate with supervisor. | 9 | *144*

E-04 Comply with applicable legal, regulatory and workplace reporting requirements (e.g., mandatory abuse and neglect reporting). | 10 | *160*

E-05 Comply with applicable legal, regulatory and workplace requirements for data collection, storage and transportation. | 10 | *164*

F. Professional Conduct and Scope of Practice

F-01 Describe the role of the RBT in the service delivery system. | 1 | *8*

F-02 Respond appropriately to feedback and maintain or improve performance accordingly | 9 | *148*

F-03 Communicate with stakeholders (e.g., family, caregivers, other professionals) as authorized. | 9 | *152*

F-04 Maintain professional boundaries (e.g., avoid dual relationships, conflicts of interest, social media contacts). | 10 | *168*

F-05 Maintain client dignity. | 10 | *172*

About the Authors

Ben Theisen founded TrainABA in 2014 to help people keep up with BACB® requirements. He is a BCBA® with a Master of Business Administration degree who has consulted in the ABA field for 10 years. At the time this book was published, 500 BCBAs had taken his continuing education workshops in supervision and ethics. Also at the time of publication, Mr. Theisen was a PhD student in Business Psychology at The Chicago School of Professional Psychology in Los Angeles, California. He enjoys dancing in his spare time.

Zach Bird is a BCBA and partner at TrainABA. He earned a Master of Science degree in Applied Behavior Analysis (ABA) while working at New England Center for Children. He has consulted for clients and organizations in United Arab Emirates, Southern California, and Massachusetts. Mr. Bird is working on his PhD in Behavior Analysis at Simmons College in Boston. He loves exploring new ways to use ABA and technology for things like fitness, gaming, and learning.

Introduction
& Segment 1

First of all, congratulations on making the decision to pursue your Registered Behavior Technician (RBT™) credential. RBT™ is a prestigious title because it comes from the Behavior Analyst Certification Board® (BACB®), a credentialing body that lawmakers, insurance providers, clients, families, schools, and companies have known and trusted since 1999.

Your decision to pursue RBT™ credentialing shows that you are the kind of person who wants the best for yourself and your clients. Congratulations on holding yourself to the highest possible standard in your field. Many people say they work with behavior intervention or autism but they do not have the science and ongoing guidance of a Board Certified Behavior Analyst® supervisor to prove it. You will. As an RBT™ professional, you will be among the best at what you do. Congratulations on choosing professional development. Your clients are lucky to have you.

At the time this book was published, the RBT™ credential was so new that no RBT™s had applied for an annual renewal yet. Nobody had taken the RBT™ exam because it did not yet exist. Can you imagine? It will be interesting to look back at this book in the future.

Starting from this time of new beginnings, TrainABA is your friend and partner at work. We are here for you throughout your career as an RBT™. Together, we will help you maintain an active credential by organizing paperwork deadlines and practicing skills consistently. As a result, you will save time to do the things you enjoy.

How do I use TrainABA?

TrainABA supervision curriculum helps you with two things:

1. Paperwork Deadlines
2. Continuing Education

TRACK is what we call a supervision time tracker that keeps a signed record of your supervisor meetings each month. When your renewal date approaches, use TRACK to start working on renewal assessment and other requirements. We will update TRACK to reflect the most recent changes to the RBT™ renewal requirements but you should also be aware of the BACB® requirements as they develop over the years. Each month, we select a few skill areas to explore to help you advance your knowledge of task list items.

For the Active RBT™

Are you already an RBT™?
IF YOUR NAME IS LISTED IN THE RBT™ REGISTRY:
- ➤ Follow the schedule in this book
- ➤ Every RBT™ at your company follows the same segment, regardless of renewal date. (e.g., Segment 1 = January, Segment 2 = February… Segment 12 = December).
- ➤ Fill out workbook boxes during in your first year with this curriculum.
- ➤ Begin **Renewal Application** 45 days before your annual deadline.
- ➤ Continue the same RBT™ segment schedule at your company.

For the Future RBT™

Are you working on your RBT™ Credential?
IF YOU HAVE NOT YET FINISHED RBT™ TRAINING:
- ➤ Write in this book during your 40-Hour RBT™ Training (unless you already did it)
- ➤ Take notes in workbook boxes
- ➤ Review before taking the RBT™ Competency Assessment
- ➤ Keep book for ongoing supervision and to help you review as needed
- ➤ Take and pass the BACB® RBT™ credential exam
- ➤ Follow steps on list above ("**For the Active RBT™**")

TrainABA's Supervision Curriculum addressed BACB® requirements for the RBT™ as below:

BACB® Requirement for RBT™ Renewal Application	
RBT™ Requirement	TrainABA Solution
RBTs need supervision for 5% of behavior analytic work hours per month.	• Use book to follow monthly segments • (Keep your own records for 7 years)
Individual meeting required monthly	• Use book for individual and meeting agendas each month.
RBT™ Competency Assessment due annually	• Use book workboxes with monthly segments • Use TRACK for ongoing assessment • Use TRACK for renewal application
RBT™ Requirements are developing	• Use TRACK to stay current on changing requirements
RBTs must renew annually	• Use TRACK to organize your renewal application dates and content

What are segments?

We organized the meeting agendas and RBT Competency Assessment task list items into *segments*, or sets of related task list items. Segments insure that RBTs have passed each task list item on their annual RBT Competency Assessments.

Segments include two meeting agendas (individual and group) plus review for a monthly pre-assessment on a few skills.

One segment = One month

It takes one year for RBTs and supervisors to complete the curriculum in this book with their supervisors.

Your supervisor may ask you to focus on other task list items in a given month to help you with something specific. In that case,

continue with the monthly segment material in addition to what your supervisor requests. You will be extra smart by the end of that month.

Renewal

You will organize renewal paperwork with TRACK, a cloud-based supervision curriculum software. RBTs can prepare for the annual renewal assessment by reviewing written notes in the book. Practice at home on a sibling, pet, roommate, etc. Get out the tape recorder and interview yourself with practice questions.

You can do the whole assessment in under one hour if you are prepared. If you miss an assessment item, the BACB® requests that your supervisor wait until the next day to try again.

Onward

We organized the deliverables – what you need to give the BACB® -- on the following page. The rest of this book presents a set of 12 segments, encapsulating all of your required review items. Do you remember how long we said it will take you to finish this book? One year.

Your RBT training is an opportunity to grow both personally and professionally. As one of the first RBTs, you are making history as a direct care provider of the only scientifically proven treatment for autism. You may know that applied behavior analysis (ABA) works for so much more than autism.

You can use ABA principles on yourself, too. Ben, one of the authors of this book, lost 92 pounds while practicing what he learned in ABA classes. Zach, co-author, used ABA to get his previous supervisor to use fewer exclamation points in work emails.

ABA is used in military flight training, traffic safety, casino blackjack, robotics, artificial intelligence, dance, special education, animal behavior, and more. You can discover new ways to do things better in your daily life. ABA gives you the power to change what is going on around you. Exciting, right? Ah! What will you do with ABA?

Deliverables for Supervisor

The BACB® registry matches an RBT to a BCBA or BCaBA supervisor ("Responsible Certificant"). The supervisor must maintain documentation as below:

1. Original documentation of ongoing supervision
    a. Two meeting dates
    b. At least one meeting was individual supervision
    c. At least one meeting included direct observation of RBT™ with client
    d. Group supervision includes up to 10 RBTs per meeting
    e. Record of supervision for 5% of ABA service hours
    f. **(Use TRACK to record supervision hours on your phone via TrainABA.com.)**

In the *TrainABA Supervision Curriculum: RBT Credential* system, supervisors do items above AND:

2. Fill out Scorecard checklist
    a. Scorecard verifies that you received all of your RBT's deliverables for a segment
3. Run the Individual and/or Group Meetings by following the agendas
4. Assess
    a. Assess the supervisee on the segment items that month (average of 3 items per month)
    b. Record assessment with TRACK (on http://trainaba.com/TRACK) or in your RBT's book

Deliverables for RBT

After you pass the RBT Exam, you must:

1. Maintain your own documentation as below
    a. 40-hour training certificate
    b. RBT Competency Assessment
        i. Annual renewal required – use TRACK at TrainABA.com
    c. Signed attestation that you are supervised in accordance with BACB® standards
        i. Annual renewal with supervisor signature – use TRACK at TrainABA.com
2. Pass the board exam

In the *TrainABA Supervision Curriculum* system, supervisees do items above AND:

3. Complete all items on the Scorecard checklist (found at start of each segment)
4. Attend Individual and/or Group Meetings
5. Fill out Workbook Boxes for current segment
6. Pass assessment for each task list item in segment for that month
    a. Your supervisor may provide additional work to help you score well on the assessment for items in that segment.

If you complete everything, your supervisor will check all the boxes on your segment **scorecard**.

Segment 1 – Scorecard Introduction

(Supervisor checks boxes)

☐ Individual Supervision
☐ Group Supervision

F 1
☐ Assessment
☐ Workbook boxes completed

B 1
☐ Assessment
☐ Workbook boxes completed

D 2
☐ Assessment
☐ Workbook boxes completed

Segment 1 – Individual Supervision Agenda

Supervisor: _____ **Technician:** _____

Meeting Date: _____ **Time of meeting – From:** _____ **To:** _____

This document covers supervisory period from _____/_____/_____ **to** _____/_____/_____

1. Review Workbook Boxes:

    Has supervisee satisfactorily completed workbook boxes?   Yes / No

- If not, what is needed to complete boxes? Describe below

2. Task List items addressed (F 1; B 1; D 2)

3. Describe/Discuss task list items with technician

4. Discussion topics or activities completed during this meeting:

Evaluation of Technician's Performance				
(Record: S- "Satisfactory"; NI- "Needs Improvement"; U- "Unsatisfactory"; or NA- "Not Applicable")				
Arrived on time for meeting		Gave examples as needed		
Completed workbook boxes		Accepted supervisory feedback appropriately		
Referred to task list item		Answered all questions thoroughly		
Maintained professional communication during supervision meeting				
Overall evaluation of supervisee performance during this meeting *(Circle one—use code above)*			S NI U	
If "NI" or "U", please list corrective steps needed to achieve a score of "S"				

5. Practice assigned for next meeting

6. Closing questions/feedback

Segment 1 – Group Supervision Meeting Agenda

- <u>Meeting Topic</u>: Introduction

- <u>Segment 1 Task List Items</u>:
- F-01: Describe the role of the RBT in the service delivery system.

- B-01: Define and provide examples of behavior and the environment in observable and measurable terms.
- D-02: Describe common functions of behavior.

1. Housekeeping
   - Take attendance for the meeting.
   - State the duration of today's meeting.
   - *Provide an overview of how supervision works.*
   - Provide an overview of materials needed for supervision.
2. Task List Lesson
   - Discuss task list item F-01: Describe the role of the RBT in the service delivery system.
   - Discuss task list item B-01: Define and provide examples of behavior and the environment in observable and measurable terms.
   - Discuss task litem item D-02: Describe common functions of behavior.
3. Workbook Boxes
   - Discuss expectations for workbook boxes.
     1. Purpose of workbooks boxes is to help technician pass and review for annual RBT Competency Assessment, which must be signed and completed within 45 days of renewal application
     2. RBT Competency Assessment was first completed for RBT application and must be updated annually with each renewal application
     3. Assessment does not need to be completed all at once. Multiple sessions are okay. TrainABA's system walks the technician through pre-assessments at one segment per month so as not to overwhelm the RBT. However, RBTs are expected to meet RBT assessment criteria by the end of each segment. Each RBT must complete an annual RBT Task List Assessment within 45 days of renewal each year. We will practice a few of these items each month to refresh skills and expand your mastery of the task list items.
     4. It is normal to lose skills that are not practiced. Supervision is a time to practice and explore new applications for concepts you already know.
     5. Feedback is a good thing. It helps you improve.
     6. Complete workbook boxes in your first year.
     7. Review the material every year following to refresh your memory and pass your assessment.
4. Questions
   - Answer any questions related to the workbook boxes or topics discussed.
5. Closing Notes
   - Close the meeting by inviting supervisees to request topics to be covered in upcoming meetings.

F – 01 DESCRIBE THE ROLE OF THE RBT IN THE SERVICE DELIVERY SYSTEM.

What is it?

The Registered Behavior Technician (RBT) is a credential for working in behavioral settings. RBTs maintain records with the Behavior Analyst Certification Board®, or BACB®. The RBT is the direct link between the client and behavioral program. RBTs provide *direct implementation,* or running behavioral programs designed by a behavior analyst supervisor. The RBT runs the programs, collecting data directly.

The relationship between a BCBA supervisor and RBT could be compared to a doctor and nurse. A doctor has special university training to diagnose problems and write treatment plans. Some patients can follow plans on their own (i.e., filling a prescription and taking a pill daily). Other patients have trouble caring for themselves and rely on nurses for help with treatment plans. BCBAs are like the doctors who use their special university training to write treatment plans for behavior. Just as a nurse knows how to "read the chart," RBTs are specially trained to understand and help carry out the treatment plan. It is very important that RBTs follow the plan as directed by the BCBA.

BACB® credentials (BCBA, BCaBA, and RBT) are recognized worldwide. The credential helps insurance companies and schools know what training and knowledge you have. In some areas, BCaBAs are rare. In such situations, RBTs are supervised directly by BCBAs. The hierarchy is shown in the chart below:

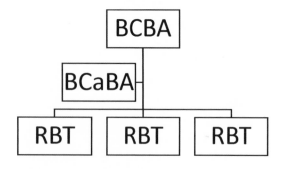

Both BCBAs and BCaBAs can supervise RBTs. It is not unusual to see a BCBA or BCaBA supervising 10-20 RBTs, depending on location.

Example 1:

Mikey, a 6-year old boy from California, was diagnosed with autism last week. His mother wanted him to have the best treatment available. One school had paraprofessionals with behavior training, yet she did not know how much knowledge or training they had. Another school required teachers to hold a BCBA or BCaBA credential. The paraprofessionals held RBT credentials. Mikey's mother chose the school that required BACB® credentials. She knew exactly what training the school staff had and was impressed by the BACB® Compliance Code. Ethical, professional care was important to her.

Example 2:

A BCBA supervisor wrote a behavior plan to reduce spitting. The insurance company only gave the BCBA 10 hours per month to provide supervision. The BCBA gave the plan to the RBT, who had enough training to know how to run the program. When the plan was not working, the RBT knew how to describe the problem to the BCBA supervisor. The supervisor asked the RBT to make the data into graphs. After a few weeks, the program successfully reduced spitting behavior because the RBT was there to carry out the plan. Can you guess who was most excited the plan worked? The RBT. She was tired of getting spit on by the client and was glad it finally stopped. The RBT knew how important her job was. Without the RBT, there was a missing link in the chain of behavioral services. The supervisor alone did not have enough hours in her schedule to help the child practice her program successfully.

Example 3:

A BCBA supervisor playfully asked her best RBT to conduct a functional behavioral assessment (FBA) independently. "Yeah, right," the RBT laughed. "Let me get a master's degree and I'll get right back to you…" The BCBA laughed and said, "Right? Too funny. I know FBAs are outside your scope of practice as an RBT. I just think you are doing well in your role and wanted to encourage you to think about pursuing university coursework if this career is part of your long term plan."

Describe/discuss this item.

Write more examples.

F-01 ASSESSMENT

(Supervisor only)

<u>Criteria</u>: *Interview*

<u>Assessment:</u>
- Ask technician to describe the clinical hierarchy for BCBAs, BCaBAs, and RBTs (above chart).
- Ask technician to discuss how the role of BCBA or BCaBA and RBT is like a doctor and nurse.
- Ask technician to describe role of RBT in service delivery at your specific workplace.
- Ask technician what she would do if she did not agree with one of your behavior plans, or thought it was not effective?

Notes:

Assessment notes:

Notes:

B –01 DESCRIBE BEHAVIOR AND ENVIRONMENT IN OBSERVABLE AND MEASUREABLE TERMS.

Definitions:

Behavior - "The activity of living organisms; human behavior includes everything that people do" (Cooper, Heron, & Heward, 2007, p. 690).

Environment – "Everything except the moving parts of the organism" (Johnston & Pennypacker, 1993a, p. 9).

Dead man's test – "If a dead man can do it, it ain't behavior. And if a dead man can't do it, then it is behavior" (Malott & Trogan Suarez, 2004, p. 9) .

Why is this important?

The relation between the environment and behavior is what behavior analysts study. As an RBT, it is important that you pay very close attention to how the environment is interacting with the behavior of your clients. This helps so you can relay this information to your BCBA supervisor.

When your supervisor works on developing definitions for behavior that you may be collecting data on, she works on making it something you can observe and then measure. Good definitions probably do not include things you cannot see or hear.

Example 1:

Your supervisor wrote a definition for aggression. She defined it as "any instance of Seth hitting another person with his closed fist from more than 6 inches away. Does not include fist bumping another person as a greeting or praise."

Example 2:

The parent of your client is interested in collecting data on when her daughter is "mad" during session. She asks you to help create a definition that she can discuss with the supervisor when she comes out next week. You ask her to specify the behavior she sees when she talks about your client being "mad". You agree to discuss adding "crying" to your data collection next week with the supervisor.

Describe/ discuss this item.

Write more examples.

B – 01 ASSESSMENT

(Supervisor only)

<u>Criteria</u>: *Interview*

<u>Assessment:</u>
- Ask technician to discuss how she can tell whether something is a behavior or not (Dead man's test or definition of "behavior").
- Ask technician to describe the role environment plays in relation to behavior.
- Ask technician to create a definition for a response she may encounter at your work environment. Ensure that the definition is clear, objective, and complete.

Notes:

Assessment notes:

Notes:

D –02 DESCRIBE COMMON FUNCTIONS OF BEHAVIOR.

Definitions:
Reinforcer - "A stimulus change that increases the future frequency of behavior that immediately precedes it" (Cooper, Heron, & Heward, 2007, p. 702).

Why is this important?
When attempting to understand why behavior occurs, we often speak about what a particular response *produces*. Does it produce attention? Does it produce escape from tasks? Does it produce some sort of sensory experience that the individual likes? We describe consequences that are produced as "functions".

When behavior analysts talk about functions they are typically discussing what type of stimulation will function as a reinforcer for that response.

The important thing to remember about a reinforcer is that it increases the future probability of a particular response.

The types of reinforcers can be categorized in several ways but we will discuss one particular way we have found to be useful:

Socially mediated reinforcement
(requires another person to deliver)
Examples-
- Attention –
    - Student: Raises hand
    - Teacher: "Yes, Johnny?"
- Escape from unpreferred environments –
    - Student: "Can I have a 5-minute break?"
    - Teacher: "Sure. Thanks for asking."
- Tangible items/activities
    - At an ice cream shop, I order a chocolate swirl and the person behind the counter prepares it and hands it to me.

Automatic reinforcement
(does not require another person to deliver)
Examples –
- Escape from unpreferred environments
    - I'm at a concert and the music is too loud. I walk outside to get away from the noise.
- Tangible items/activities
    - I see my iPad on the table. I walk over and pick it up.
- Sensory
    - When I'm in the bathroom by myself, I pretend my hairbrush is a microphone and I dance in the mirror.

Describe/ discuss this item.

Write more examples.

D – 02 ASSESSMENT

(Supervisor only)

Criteria: *Interview*

Assessment:

- Ask technician to define "reinforcer".
- Ask technician to describe some types of reinforcement.
- Give some examples of behavior that occurs at your workplace and ask technician to provide a guess about the function of that particular response.

Notes:

Assessment notes:

Notes:

Segment 2 – Scorecard Measurement

(Supervisor checks boxes)

☐ Individual Supervision
☐ Group Supervision

A 1
☐ Assessment
☐ Workbook boxes completed

A 3
☐ Assessment
☐ Workbook boxes completed

A 2
☐ Assessment
☐ Workbook boxes completed

A 4
☐ Assessment
☐ Workbook boxes completed

Segment 2 – Individual Supervision Agenda

Supervisor: _____ **Technician:** _____

Meeting Date: _____ **Time of meeting – From:**_____ **To:**_____

This document covers supervisory period from ____/____/____ **to** ____/____/____

1. Review Workbook Boxes:

    Has supervisee satisfactorily completed workbook boxes?   Yes / No

- If not, what is needed to complete boxes? Describe below

2. Task List items addressed (A 1-4)

3. Describe/Discuss task list items with technician

4. Discussion topics or activities completed during this meeting:

Evaluation of Technician's Performance				
(Record: S- "Satisfactory"; NI- "Needs Improvement"; U- "Unsatisfactory"; or NA- "Not Applicable")				
Arrived on time for meeting		Gave examples as needed		
Completed workbook boxes		Accepted supervisory feedback appropriately		
Referred to task list item		Answered all questions thoroughly		
Maintained professional communication during supervision meeting				
Overall evaluation of supervisee performance during this meeting *(Circle one—use code above)*			S NI U	
If "NI" or "U", please list corrective steps needed to achieve a score of "S"				

5. Practice assigned for next meeting

6. Closing questions/feedback

Segment 2 – Group Supervision Meeting Agenda

- <u>Meeting Topic</u>: Measurement

- <u>Task List Items Reviewed</u>:

- A-01: Describe how to prepare for data collection.
- A-02: Implement continuous measurement procedures (e.g., frequency, duration).

- A-03: Implement discontinuous measurement procedures (e.g., partial & whole interval, momentary time sampling).
- A-04: Implement permanent product recording procedures.

1. Housekeeping
   - Take attendance.
   - State the duration of today's meeting.
2. Task List Lesson and Discussion
   - Discuss task list item A-01: Describe how to prepare for data collection.
   - Discuss task list item A-02: Implement continuous measurement procedures (e.g., frequency, duration).
   - Discuss task list item A-03: Implement discontinuous measurement procedures (e.g., partial & whole interval, momentary time sampling).
   - Discuss task list item A-04: Implement permanent product recording procedures.
3. Segment Review
   - Review segment items from current meeting
   - Review workbook boxes from RBTs to generate discussion
   - When presenting material, use response cards and ask frequent questions (raise hand, write on a paper and hold up the answer, etc.)
   - Use behavioral skills training to keep information interactive.
   - Include role play at every group meeting and do not rely on lecture for the bulk of meeting.
   - Raise specific case examples. Provide enough context for others in group to understand the idiosyncrasies of case. Do not dominate the time by discussing one or a handful of clients. Cover enough material to engage all learners and evoke behavior from RBTs.
4. Questions
   - Answer any relevant questions.
   - If RBTs do not ask have questions, quiz them on what you have covered in the meeting.
5. Closing Notes
   - Reinforce writing in workbook boxes and preparation for assessment.
   - Close the meeting by inviting supervisees to request topics to be covered in upcoming meetings.

A – 01 DESCRIBE HOW TO PREPARE FOR DATA COLLECTION.

Definition:
Data - "The results of measurement…" (Cooper, Heron, & Heward, 2007, p. 693)

Why is this important?
"Without data you're just another person with an opinion."
> – W. Edwards Deming, American management consultant

Data collection is what helps us monitor progress and make sure we are using the most effective methods of intervention.
We track data about behavior that we hope to:
1. Increase
2. Decrease
3. Maintain

What do we need to collect data?
A response definition (necessary) and one or more of the following:
- Data sheet/computer w/ software
- Pen
- Watch/stopwatch
- Counter

Examples:
Types of data collection include:
- Frequency
- Duration
- Partial interval
- Whole interval
- Momentary time sample
- Percentage of opportunity
- Discrete trial data

Non-examples:
- A guess, estimate, or "guesstimate"
- Parent/caregiver opinion

Describe/ discuss this item.

Write more examples.

A – 01 DESCRIBE HOW TO PREPARE FOR DATA COLLECTION.

(Supervisor only)

<u>Criteria</u>: *Interview*

<u>Assessment</u>:
- Ask technician to define "data".
- Ask technician to describe why collecting data is important.
- Ask technician to give examples of some types of behavior he/she would measure at your workplace.
- Ask technician to describe what materials would be needed to collect data at your workplace.

Notes:

Assessment notes:

Notes:

A – 02 IMPLEMENT CONTINUOUS MEASUREMENT PROCEDURES (FREQUENCY, DURATION).

Definitions:

Frequency – how many times a response occurs in a certain period of time

Duration – a measure of time – how long a response occurs

Why is this important?

Frequency and duration are two commonly used measurement procedures. They are considered "continuous" measurement procedures because to use these types of data collection. They require the person tracking the responses to pay attention the entire time.

There are some things the supervisor takes into consideration before choosing which measure to use.

If frequency is used, it is often a response that looks similar each time it occurs. It can be easily counted.

If duration is used, it is often a response that may last a period of time that changes each time it occurs. Is that confusing? In other words, your supervisor may ask you to measure how long the client's tantrums last. You measure five tantrums. The duration of those five tantrums measured 3, 7, 25, 2, and 38 minutes. You measured the duration of those tantrums individually.

Examples - frequency:

Measure the number of math problems completed in an hour

Measure instances of profane language

Examples – duration:

Crying
Vacuuming
Tantruming
Jogging
Showering
Washing dishes
Working at a table

Describe/discuss this item.

Write more examples.

A – 02 IMPLEMENT CONTINUOUS MEASUREMENT PROCEDURES (FREQUENCY, DURATION).

(Supervisor only)

<u>Criteria</u>: *Role play*

<u>Assessment:</u>
- Roleplay a scenario that may require a **frequency** measure. Act as the client and have the technician collect data. Choose a response she is likely to see at your workplace. Please provide a datasheet for the technician.
- Roleplay a scenario that may require a **duration** measure. Act as the client and have the technician collect data. Choose a response she is likely to see at your workplace. Please provide a datasheet for the technician.

Notes:

Assessment notes:

NOTES:

A – 03 IMPLEMENT DISCONTINUOUS MEASUREMENT PROCEDURES (E.G., PARTIAL AND WHOLE INTERVAL, MOMENTARY TIME SAMPLING)

Definition:

Partial interval - "a time sampling method…The observer records whether the target behavior occurred at any time during the interval." (Cooper, Heron, & Heward, 2007, p. 701)

Whole interval - "a time sampling method…The observer records whether the target behavior occurred throughout the entire interval." (Cooper, Heron, & Heward, 2007, p. 708)

Momentary time sampling - A measurement method in which the observer records whether or not the target behavior is occurring at the moment the interval ends.

Why is this important?

Discontinuous measurement procedures are methods of collecting data that do not require as much effort to collect. These methods sample parts of the day to get an estimate of how often a response is occurring.

Advantages:

- Requires data collection once per interval rather than every instance
- Is sometimes easier if you have many things to manage besides data collection
- Is sometimes preferred by those collecting the data

Disadvantages:

- Does not collect all instances of behavior
- May over or under estimate the response

Example 1:

Partial interval data are being collected on Terry's screaming. The data are being collected in 10 minute intervals. If Terry screams at any point during the 10-minute interval, a (+) is written on the datasheet. Nothing else needs to be written until the next interval. If no screaming occurs during the 10 minutes, a (–) is written for that interval.

Example 2:

Whole interval data are being collected on Jamie's on-task behavior. The data are being collected in 5 minute intervals. If Jamie is on-task during the entire 5 minutes, a (+) is written on the datasheet for that interval. If Jamie starts joking around in class or starts talking with his friend at any point during the interval, a (–) is written on the datasheet. If that occurs, nothing else needs to be written until the next interval.

Example 3:

Momentary time sampling is being used to collected data on Ben's phone use. The data are collected in 2 minute intervals. Zach sets a timer for 2 minutes. When the timer goes off, Zach looks at Ben. If Ben is using his phone when the timer goes off, a (+) is written on the datasheet. If Ben is not using his phone when the timer goes off, a (–) is written on the datasheet.

Describe/discuss this item.

Write more examples.

A – 03 IMPLEMENT DISCONTINUOUS MEASUREMENT PROCEDURES (E.G., PARTIAL AND WHOLE INTERVAL, MOMENTARY TIME SAMPLING).

(Supervisor only)

Criteria: *Role play*

Assessment:

- Roleplay a scenario that may require a **partial interval measure**. Act as the client and have the technician collect data. Choose a response she is likely to see at your workplace. Please provide a datasheet for the technician.
- Roleplay a scenario that may require a **whole interval measure**. Act as the client and have the technician collect data. Choose a response she is likely to see at your workplace. Please provide a datasheet for the technician.
- Roleplay a scenario that may require **momentary time sampling**. Act as the client and have the technician collect data. Choose a response she is likely to see at your workplace. Please provide a datasheet for the technician.

REMEMBER: For this part of the assessment, the technician only needs to show competency with A-03 OR A-04, not both.

Notes:

Assessment notes:

Notes:

A – 04 IMPLEMENT PERMANENT PRODUCT RECORDING PROCEDURES

Definition:

Permanent product recording - "A method of measuring behavior after it has occurred by recording the effects that the behavior produced on the environment." (Cooper, Heron, & Heward, 2007, p. 699)

Why is this important?

Sometimes it is easier to collect data on the environment after a response occurs. This is called permanent product recording. Most of our traditional education system is built on this type of data collection. Your teacher will hand you a worksheet and then when you pass it in, she will grade it. She will put that grade into her datasheet (gradebook) and then at the end of the quarter, send a progress report to your house. Your teacher did not watch you while you completed your assignment. She recorded data – usually a percentage of correct answers – on a permanent product of your work. This was more efficient than watching each individual student complete the worksheet while collecting the data.

Examples:

Types of activities that may allow for permanent product recording include:

- Putting together a puzzle – pieces put together
- Coloring – pages of a coloring book
- Smoking - cigarette butts in an ashtray
- Raking leaves – piles of leaves
- Cleaning tables – number of clean tables
- Hanging up clothes – number of clothes on hangers

Describe/discuss this item.

Write more examples.

A – 04 IMPLEMENT PERMANENT PRODUCT RECORDING PROCEDURES

(Supervisor only)

<u>Criteria</u>: *Role play*

<u>Assessment:</u>

- Roleplay a scenario that may allow for a **permanent product recording procedure**. Act as the client and have the technician collect data. Choose a response she is likely to see at your workplace. Please provide materials and a datasheet for the technician.

  REMEMBER: For this part of the assessment, the technician only needs to show competency with A-03 OR A-04, not both.

Notes:

Assessment notes:

Notes:

Segment 3 – Scorecard
Skill Acquisition I

(Supervisor checks boxes)

☐ Individual Supervision
☐ Group Supervision

C 1
☐ Assessment
☐ Workbook boxes completed

C 2
☐ Assessment
☐ Workbook boxes completed

C 3
☐ Assessment
☐ Workbook boxes completed

Segment 3 – Individual Supervision Agenda

Supervisor: _____ **Technician:** _____

Meeting Date: _____ **Time of meeting – From:**_____ **To:**_____

This document covers supervisory period from ____/____/____ to ____/____/____

1. Review Workbook Boxes:

    Has supervisee satisfactorily completed workbook boxes?   Yes / No

- If not, what is needed to complete boxes? Describe below

2. Task List items addressed (C 1-3)

3. Describe/Discuss task list items with technician

4. Discussion topics or activities completed during this meeting:

Evaluation of Technician's Performance			
(Record: S- "Satisfactory"; NI- "Needs Improvement"; U- "Unsatisfactory"; or NA- "Not Applicable")			
Arrived on time for meeting		Gave examples as needed	
Completed workbook boxes		Accepted supervisory feedback appropriately	
Referred to task list item		Answered all questions thoroughly	
Maintained professional communication during supervision meeting			
Overall evaluation of supervisee performance during this meeting *(Circle one—use code above)*		S NI U	
If "NI" or "U", please list corrective steps needed to achieve a score of "S"			

5. Practice assigned for next meeting

6. Closing questions/feedback

Segment 3 – Group Supervision Meeting Agenda

- <u>Meeting Topic</u>: Skill Acquisition I

- <u>Task List Items Reviewed</u>:
- C-01 Identify the essential components of a written skill acquisition plan.
- C-02 Describe how to prepare for the session as required by the skill acquisition plan.
- C-03 Use contingencies of reinforcement (e.g., conditioned/ unconditioned reinforcement, continuous/intermittent schedules).

1. Housekeeping
   - Take attendance.
   - State the duration of today's meeting.
2. Task List Lesson and Discussion
   - Discuss task list item C-01 Identify the essential components of a written skill acquisition plan.
   - Discuss task list item C-02 Describe how to prepare for the session as required by the skill acquisition plan.
   - Discuss task list item C-03 Use contingencies of reinforcement (e.g., conditioned/ unconditioned reinforcement, continuous/intermittent schedules).
3. Segment Review
   - Review segment items from current meeting
   - Review workbook boxes from RBTs to generate discussion
   - When presenting material, use response cards and ask frequent questions (raise hand, write on a paper and hold up the answer, etc.)
   - Use behavioral skills training to keep information interactive.
   - Include role play at every group meeting and do not rely on lecture for the bulk of meeting.
   - Raise specific case examples. Provide enough context for others in group to understand the idiosyncrasies of case. Do not dominate the time by discussing one or a handful of clients. Cover enough material to engage all learners and evoke behavior from RBTs.
4. Questions
   - Answer any relevant questions.
   - If RBTs do not ask have questions, quiz them on what you have covered in the meeting.
5. Closing Notes
   - Reinforce writing in workbook boxes and preparation for assessment.
   - Close the meeting by inviting supervisees to request topics to be covered in upcoming meetings.

C – 01 IDENTIFY THE ESSENTIAL COMPONENTS OF A SKILL ACQUISITION PLAN

Definition:
Skill acquisition plan - a document that contains information about behavior programming designed to teach skills

Why is this important?
One of the major goals of a behavior technician is to run the behavior plans of his clients. Some behavior plans are designed to decrease behavior while others are designed to increase a certain skill set. Some plans are a combination of the two.

Depending on where you work, a skill acquisition plan can look very different. There are certain shared characteristics of most skill acquisition plans that we can describe here.

Company-specific plans will be given to you by your supervisor.

Most skill acquisition plans include:
- Description of each target skill
- Instruction or context for teaching
- Materials needed for teaching
- Prompting strategy
- Consequence for correct responses
- Consequence for incorrect responses
- Criteria for mastery
- Plan for generalization
- Plan for thinning of reinforcement schedule

Examples:
Examples of skill acquisition plans can be requested from your supervisor

Describe/ discuss this item.

Write more examples.

C – 01 IDENTIFY THE ESSENTIAL COMPONENTS OF A SKILL ACQUISITION PLAN

(Supervisor only)

Criteria: *Interview*

Assessment:

- Ask technician to define "skill acquisition plan"
- Ask technician to describe why having a skill acquisition plan is important
- Ask technician to describe the essential components of your company-specific skill acquisition plan.

Notes:

Assessment notes:

NOTES:

C – 02 DESCRIBE HOW TO PREPARE FOR THE SESSION AS REQUIRED BY THE SKILL ACQUISITION PLAN.

Why is this important?
Now that you can identify the essential components of a skill acquisition plan, it's time to talk about using one.

Each company/institution will have its own requirements for how your time with clients is spent but there are a few things that almost all companies/institutions share.

When you are preparing for a session, try to have these things ready before starting:
- Instructions for the program you are running
- Materials for teaching (DTT stimuli or props)
- Materials for data collection (pen and paper; iPad)
- High preference items to deliver as reinforcers

Example 1:
Karen is an RBT. She works with Jacob two afternoons per week. One of Jacob's goals is to brush his teeth. Karen always checks the skill acquisition plan for any changes that might have been made by her supervisor since her last visit. This also helps refresh her memory about what instruction to give and what prompt level to use. Before asking Jacob to brush his teeth, she makes sure the toothbrush and toothpaste are in the bathroom. She grabs her datasheet and pen and gets one of Jacob's favorite toys (to deliver as a reinforcer). She does all these things *before* asking Jacob to brush his teeth. Her preparations give him the best chance of success when he gets to the sink to brush his teeth.

Example 2:
Derek is also an RBT. He works with Eliza each day after she gets out of school. One of her objectives is to say hi to him when he walks into the house. Before walking into the home, he checks the skill acquisition plan to see what prompt level to use. He is working on fading out his prompt so that she can become independent. He gets a small piece of candy he keeps in his glove compartment to deliver when she responds. He keeps the datasheet on the wall right inside the door with a pen attached with a string. This way he can take data right after he greets her.

Describe/ discuss this item.

Write more examples.

C – 02 DESCRIBE HOW TO PREPARE FOR THE SESSION AS REQUIRED BY THE SKILL ACQUISITION PLAN.

(Supervisor only)

Criteria: *Interview*

Assessment:

- Ask technician to describe why it is important to prepare for the session before starting with a client.
- Ask technician to describe what steps he should take to prepare for a session at your company/institution.

Notes:

Assessment notes:

Notes:

C – 03 USE CONTINGENCIES OF REINFORCEMENT (E.G., CONDITIONED/UNCONDITIONED REINFORCEMENT, CONTINUOUS/INTERMITTENT SCHEDULES.)

Definition:

Unconditioned reinforcer – A reinforcer that does not need to be taught/learned. Liquid to drink and air to breathe are examples.

Conditioned reinforcer – A reinforcer that gets its value by being paired with another reinforcer.

Continuous reinforcement (CRF or FR1) – "A schedule of reinforcement that provides reinforcement for each occurrence of the target behavior" (Cooper, Heron, & Heward, 2007, p. 693).

Intermittent reinforcement – "A contingency of reinforcement in which some, but not all, occurrences of the behavior produce reinforcement" (Cooper, Heron, & Heward, 2007, p.698)

Why is this important?

Reinforcement contingencies are what teach and maintain all behavior that we learn during a lifetime. When we look to teach skills we need to make sure we provide reinforcement to help learning occur.

Certain reinforcers are part of any living thing's DNA. They are called "unconditioned reinforcers" because they do not need to be taught/conditioned.

Examples may include:
- Food when hungry
- Water when thirsty
- Sex and orgasm
- Escape from pain
- Physical attention

Other reinforcers require previous pairing to become reinforcers. These are called "conditioned reinforcers".

Examples may include:
- Tokens
- Money
- Praise
- Grades
- High fives
- Stickers

The way that we deliver reinforcers matters. Sometimes we want to make sure that we deliver them every time a response occurs. This is called "continuous reinforcement". We would often use this for when we want to teach something.

When we simply want to maintain a skill, or fade out reinforcement, we will change the schedule of reinforcement to an "intermittent schedule". An intermittent schedule of reinforcement is one in which we do not deliver a reinforcer after every response. We may reinforce every second or third response.

Describe/discuss this item.

Write more examples.

C – 03 USE CONTINGENCIES OF REIN-FORCEMENT (E.G., CONDITIONED/UN-CONDITIONED REINFORCEMENT, CONTINUOUS/INTERMITTENT SCHEDULES.)

(Supervisor only)

Criteria: *Role play*

Assessment:

- Roleplay a scenario that requires the technician to delivery reinforcers in a variety of arrangements. Act as the client and have the technician reinforce responses using conditioned reinforcement and unconditioned reinforcement on continuous schedules and intermittent schedules. We recommend that you say something like "I'll pretend to do some homework and you reinforce correct math problem completion using an X reinforcer on a Y schedule of reinforcement." Create several examples to confirm that the technician can use each type and schedule as you would at your specific workplace.

Notes:

Assessment notes:

Notes:

Segment 4 – Scorecard
Skill Acquisition II

(Supervisor checks boxes)

☐ Individual Supervision
☐ Group Supervision

C 4
☐ Assessment
☐ Workbook boxes completed

C 5
☐ Assessment
☐ Workbook boxes completed

C 6
☐ Assessment
☐ Workbook boxes completed

Segment 4 – Individual Supervision Agenda

Supervisor: _____ **Technician:** _____

Meeting Date: _____ **Time of meeting – From:** _____ **To:** _____

This document covers supervisory period from ____/____/____ to ____/____/____

1. Review Workbook Boxes:

    Has supervisee satisfactorily completed workbook boxes?   Yes / No

    • If not, what is needed to complete boxes? Describe below

2. Task List items addressed (C 4-6)

```
[                                                                ]
[                                                                ]
[                                                                ]
[                                                                ]
[                                                                ]
```

3. Describe/Discuss task list items with technician

```
[                                                                ]
[                                                                ]
[                                                                ]
[                                                                ]
```

4. Discussion topics or activities completed during this meeting:

Evaluation of Technician's Performance				
(Record: S- "Satisfactory"; NI- "Needs Improvement"; U- "Unsatisfactory"; or NA- "Not Applicable")				
Arrived on time for meeting		Gave examples as needed		
Completed workbook boxes		Accepted supervisory feedback appropriately		
Referred to task list item		Answered all questions thoroughly		
Maintained professional communication during supervision meeting				
Overall evaluation of supervisee performance during this meeting (Circle one—use code above)			S NI U	
If "NI" or "U", please list corrective steps needed to achieve a score of "S"				

5. Practice assigned for next meeting

```
[                                                                ]
[                                                                ]
[                                                                ]
[                                                                ]
```

6. Closing questions/feedback

```
[                                                                ]
[                                                                ]
[                                                                ]
[                                                                ]
```

Segment 4 – Group Supervision Meeting Agenda

- <u>Meeting Topic</u>: Skill Acquisition II

- <u>Task List Items Reviewed</u>:

- C-04 Implement discrete trial training procedures.
- C-05 Implement naturalistic teaching procedures (e.g., incidental teaching.)
- C-06 Implement task analyzed chaining procedures.

1. Housekeeping
   - Take attendance.
   - State the duration of today's meeting.

2. Task List Lesson and Discussion
   - Discuss task list item C-04 Implement discrete trial training procedures.
   - Discuss task list item C-05 Implement naturalistic teaching procedures (e.g., incidental teaching.)
   - Discuss task list item C-06 Implement task analyzed chaining procedures.

3. Segment Review
   - Review segment items from current meeting
   - Review workbook boxes from RBTs to generate discussion
   - When presenting material, use response cards and ask frequent questions (raise hand, write on a paper and hold up the answer, etc.)
   - Use behavioral skills training to keep information interactive.
   - Include role play at every group meeting and do not rely on lecture for the bulk of meeting.
   - Raise specific case examples. Provide enough context for others in group to understand the idiosyncrasies of case. Do not dominate the time by discussing one or a handful of clients. Cover enough material to engage all learners and evoke behavior from RBTs.

4. Questions
   - Answer any relevant questions.
   - If RBTs do not ask have questions, quiz them on what you have covered in the meeting.

5. Closing Notes
   - Reinforce writing in workbook boxes and preparation for assessment.
   - Close the meeting by inviting supervisees to request topics to be covered in upcoming meetings.

C – 04 IMPLEMENT DISCRETE TRIAL TRAINING PROCEDURES

Why is this important?

Many ABA programs are designed to teach individuals who have learning difficulties. Often traditional methods of teaching do not allow the individual to access lessons that are broken down into small enough skills that will effectively teach them. They may also not get access to enough practice to master the skill being taught. A very successful way to teach this type of learner is using discrete trial training procedures (or DTT).

There are many variations of DTT. Common properties of DTT procedures are listed below.

All discrete trial training procedures include:

- Event or instruction that we hope will control the response in the end
  - Example – "James, touch red."
- Response
  - Example – (James touches red)
- Consequence
  - Examples – "Red it is, James! Nice touching red. Here's a token for touching red." ****
- Data collection

Many discrete trial training procedures also include:

- Prompt – to make the target response more likely
- Error correction – if response is incorrect

> *You will receive extra training on the specific procedures used at your workplace.*

****Notice that I said "red" three times after James did it. You may be thinking, "Why did you say it so much when he already gave the right answer?" The reason is that a DTT program would provide a small "field" of items, such as three cards. If James guessed, he would have a 33% chance of being right. When many clients are learning with DTT, it helps to continue talking about the correct response to help the learner associate what he did – touching one of the things on the table – with the words I used – "touching red" or just "red". DTT is done many,

many times. I may ask James to "touch red" hundreds or perhaps over a thousand times. Saying the word "red" as I provide reinforcement – a sip of juice, tickles, arm shakes, etc. -- helps him learn. It also makes learning more fun because he is contacting reinforcement for responding correctly. (Note: I would be unlikely to say "red" as a consequence if I was reviewing a mastered item with James because it would not be necessary. There are other situations where it would not be necessary to say "red", which my supervisor would let me know about.)

Describe/discuss this item.

Write more examples.

C – 04 IMPLEMENT DISCRETE TRIAL TRAINING PROCEDURES

(Supervisor only)

<u>Criteria</u>: *Role play*

<u>Assessment:</u>

- Roleplay a discrete trial training session according to the procedures used at your specific workplace. Require the technician to talk you through what he is doing as he is doing it. Please provide materials and a datasheet for the technician.

  REMEMBER: For this part of the assessment, the technician only needs to show competency with C-04 OR C-05 OR C-06, not all.

Notes:

Assessment notes:

NOTES:

C – 05 IMPLEMENT NATURALISTIC TEACHING PROCEDURES (E.G., INCIDENTAL TEACHING)

Why is this important?
Incidental teaching procedures (sometimes called "natural environment training" or "NET") are often used in ABA programs to provide learning opportunities in a more naturalistic arrangement than seen in a discrete trial training session. Is that explanation too technical? Think about it. Sometimes skills are originally taught in a discrete trial session, then brought to the natural environments. As Zach says, "That makes generalization more likely to occur." Some clients do not require the strict training procedures offered by discrete trial sessions. They may learn well in a natural setting as long as there are some extra supports in place to promote learning.

Your supervisor will decide which learning arrangement will likely work best for each particular client.

What happens when your client responds correctly during incidental teaching? Instructions may still be given, data are still collected, and you arrange for a reinforcer. You may also need to deliver prompts and error correction procedures.

Example 1:
Sarah has learned to engage in conversation about what she did at school that day. She is very good at making eye contact, orienting toward the speaker, and speaking clearly when she is at the work table. The BCBA supervising Sarah's case decided it was time to work on engaging in conversation with other people and outside of her work area.

Example 2:
Anna is an RBT who worked with Thomas on learning colors. He could identify colors on cards at a worktable but his mom said he struggled at identifying colors outside of the home. Anna's supervisor has asked her to work on identifying colors on the playground. When Anna and Thomas are at the playground, Thomas loved to swing. Anna gave Thomas a push after – and only after – he answered one of her questions related to identifying colors. Sometimes she asked him what color a neighbor's house was. Sometimes it was the color of a car driving by. When Thomas answered a question correctly, Anna gave him a big push. While he was swinging, she quickly collected data on her iPad.

Describe/discuss this item.

Write more examples.

C – 05 IMPLEMENT NATURALISTIC TEACHING PROCEDURES (E.G., INCIDENTAL TEACHING)

(Supervisor only)

<u>Criteria</u>: *Role play*

<u>Assessment:</u>

- Roleplay an incidental teaching session according to the procedures used at your specific workplace. Require the technician to talk you through what he is doing. Please provide materials and a datasheet for the technician.

  REMEMBER: For this part of the assessment, the technician only needs to show competency with C-04 OR C-05 OR C-06, not all.

Notes:

Assessment notes:

Notes:

C – 06 IMPLEMENT TASK ANALYZED CHAINING PROCEDURES

Definition:
Task analysis – "the process of breaking a complex skill… into smaller, teachable units" (Cooper, Heron, & Heward, 2007, p. 706).

Forward chaining procedure – a task analysis used to teach independence from the beginning to the end of a sequence

Backward chaining procedure – a task analysis used to teach independence from the end to the beginning of a sequence

Why is this important?
In ABA, we often are asked to teach complex behavior like brushing teeth, washing hands, making a sandwich, etc. When teaching individuals with learning difficulties to engage in complex behavior, we need to teach slowly and systematically. One way of doing this is by using a task analysis procedure. We will break a task down into a series of responses that we "chain" together. There are differences in the way behavior chains are taught from one workplace to another, however, there are commonly used procedures that we can discuss.

A task analysis procedure has all of the characteristics of a discrete trial training procedure discussed in section C-04. We have an instruction, a target response, a prompt, reinforcer delivery, and data collection.

The difference is that we are now working on a complex response chain that involves different pieces that will be added together to create one sequence of behavior.

With forward chaining, we will work on the sequence by teaching the beginning part of the chain at first and working toward the end. In a forward chain, the reinforcer is delivered immediately after the target step.

With backward chaining, we will work on the sequence by teaching the end of the chain first and work toward the beginning. In a backward chain the reinforcer is delivered at the end of the sequence.

Example:
Following a recipe is a good example of a behavior chain. A task analysis of making a PB&J sandwich might look like this:

1. *Get peanut butter*
2. *Get jelly*
3. *Get bread*
4. *Get knife*
5. *Put two pieces of bread on plate*
6. *Spread peanut butter with knife*
7. *Clean knife*
8. *Spread jelly with knife*
9. *Put two slices of bread together*
10. *Cut sandwich into halves*
11. *Put materials away*

If this task analysis is being taught with a forward chain, we would start teaching with step 1. *Get peanut butter.* When step 1 was mastered, we would then move to step 2. *Get jelly.*

If this task analysis is being taught with a backward chain, we would start teaching with step 11. *Put materials away.* Once step 11 was mastered, we would then move to teaching step 10. *Cut sandwich into halves.*

Describe/discuss this item.

Write more examples.

C – 06 IMPLEMENT TASK ANALYZED CHAINING PROCEDURES

(Supervisor only)

Criteria: *Role play*

Assessment:

- Roleplay a task analysis teaching session according to the procedures used at your specific workplace. Require the technician to talk you through what he is doing as he does it. Please provide materials and a datasheet for the technician.

  REMEMBER: For this part of the assessment, the technician only needs to show competency with C-04 OR C-05 OR C-06, not all.

Notes:

Assessment notes:

Notes:

Segment 5 – Scorecard
Skill Acquisition III

(Supervisor checks boxes)

☐ Individual Supervision
☐ Group Supervision

C 7
☐ Assessment
☐ Workbook boxes completed

C 8
☐ Assessment
☐ Workbook boxes completed

C 9
☐ Assessment
☐ Workbook boxes completed

C 10
☐ Assessment
☐ Workbook boxes completed

Segment 5 – Individual Supervision Agenda

Supervisor: _____ **Technician:** _____

Meeting Date: _____ **Time of meeting – From:** _____ **To:** _____

This document covers supervisory period from ____/____/____ to ____/____/____

1. Review Workbook Boxes:

    Has supervisee satisfactorily completed workbook boxes?   Yes / No

- If not, what is needed to complete boxes? Describe below

2. Task List items addressed (C 7-10)

```


```

3. Describe/Discuss task list items with technician

```


```

4. Discussion topics or activities completed during this meeting:

Evaluation of Technician's Performance				
(Record: S- "Satisfactory"; NI- "Needs Improvement"; U- "Unsatisfactory"; or NA- "Not Applicable")				
Arrived on time for meeting		Gave examples as needed		
Completed workbook boxes		Accepted supervisory feedback appropriately		
Referred to task list item		Answered all questions thoroughly		
Maintained professional communication during supervision meeting				
Overall evaluation of supervisee performance during this meeting (Circle one—use code above)			S NI U	
If "NI" or "U", please list corrective steps needed to achieve a score of "S"				

5. Practice assigned for next meeting

```


```

6. Closing questions/feedback

```


```

Segment 5 – Group Supervision Meeting Agenda

- <u>Meeting Topic</u>: Skill Acquisition III

- <u>Task List Items Reviewed</u>:

- C-07 Implement discrimination training.
- C-08 Implement stimulus control transfer procedures.

- C-09 Implement stimulus fading procedures.
- C-10 Implement prompt and prompt fading procedures.

1. Housekeeping
   - Take attendance.
   - State the duration of today's meeting.
2. Task List Lesson and Discussion
   - Discuss task list item C-07 Implement discrimination training.
   - Discuss task list item C-08 Implement stimulus control transfer procedures.
   - Discuss task list item C-09 Implement stimulus fading procedures.
   - Discuss task list item C-10 Implement prompt and prompt fading procedures.
3. Segment Review
   - Review segment items from current meeting
   - Review workbook boxes from RBTs to generate discussion
   - When presenting material, use response cards and ask frequent questions (raise hand, write on a paper and hold up the answer, etc.)
   - Use behavioral skills training to keep information interactive.
   - Include role play at every group meeting and do not rely on lecture for the bulk of meeting.
   - Raise specific case examples. Provide enough context for others in group to understand the idiosyncrasies of case. Do not dominate the time by discussing one or a handful of clients. Cover enough material to engage all learners and evoke behavior from RBTs.
4. Questions
   - Answer any relevant questions.
   - If RBTs do not ask have questions, quiz them on what you have covered in the meeting.
5. Closing Notes
   - Reinforce writing in workbook boxes and preparation for assessment.
   - Close the meeting by inviting supervisees to request topics to be covered in upcoming meetings.

C – 07 IMPLEMENT DISCRIMINATION TRAINING.

Why is this important?

Discrimination training is used to teach the difference between meaningful stimuli. Many times in our lives, reinforcement is available for certain behavior only when specific stimuli are in the environment. As an example, asking for water is likely to be reinforced only if there is another person in the room willing to get it for you. Knowing the difference between when to ask and when not to ask requires a discrimination to occur.

If you think about it, most of our behavior is like this. When driving, we need discriminated behavior to occur with street signs. When ordering from a menu, crossing the street, and following a schedule, discriminated responding is required.

> Because discriminated behavior is so important in almost every area of our lives, we often work on teaching certain discriminations with our clients. Discrimination training can be done with both discrete trial sessions and incidental teaching.

Example 1:

Tara is an RBT who works with Jamal, a 9-year-old who is learning to tell time. One of the lessons is to teach Jamal to ask for a snack only after 2pm. Right now he asks every 10 minutes no matter what time it is. Tara's supervisor has implemented a discrimination training procedure to teach Jamal when asking for a snack will be reinforced and when it will not. Every time Jamal asks for a snack and it is not yet 2:00 PM, Tara goes up to the clock, points at the hour hand and asks Jamal to tell her the time. She tells him when it is ok to ask about snack.

Example 2:

Michael is an RBT who works with Derek, a 4-year-old who enjoys playing with his 11-year-old sister. His sister enjoys playing with him, too, but sometimes she wants time to herself. Michael has been working with Derek on identifying when it is ok to go into his sister's room. When the door to her bedroom is shut, Michael is not allowed in her room. When the door is open, he can go in to play. Derek goes up to his sister's door and starts to open it. Michael stops him and says, "Look, the door is shut. We'll have to come back later," then redirects Derek to another activity without his sister.

Describe/discuss this item.

Write more examples.

C – 07 IMPLEMENT DISCRIMINATION TRAINING.

(Supervisor only)

<u>Criteria</u>: *Role play*

<u>Assessment:</u>

- Roleplay a training session that requires discrimination training according to the procedures used at your specific work-place. Require the technician to talk you through what he is doing as he is doing it. Please provide materials and a datasheet for the technician.

REMEMBER: For this part of the assessment, the technician only needs to show competency with C-07 OR C-08 OR C-09 OR C-10, not all.

Notes:

Assessment notes:

NOTES:

C – 08 IMPLEMENT STIMULUS CONTROL TRANSFER PROCEDURES.

Why is this important?

We transfer stimulus control from one stimulus in the environment to another, often when fading prompts.

We call it "stimulus control transfer" because when we prompt, we need to transfer control from our prompt to something in the natural environment. We do that to make the response independent.

We can use a number of different prompts in order to do this. Your supervisor will choose the stimulus transfer procedure that will work best depending on the skill being taught and what has been successful with that client in the past. Here are a few stimulus transfer strategies:

- Most to least prompt
  - We prompt the response using the most intrusive prompt first and decrease the intrusiveness over time.

- Least to most prompt
  - We prompt the response with only the intrusiveness needed to get the response to occur.

- Prompt delay
  - We give an opportunity for the learner to respond independently before we prompt.

Example 1:

Jessie is working with Nick on making his bed. They are using a most-to-least prompting procedure. At first, Jessie had to physically prompt Nick to pull the blankets up with a full prompt. Over the last couple of trials, she was able to fade out her help so that he pulled the blankets up when she simply touched his hand.

Example 2:

Jessie is also teaching Nick to remember to dry his hands after washing them. She uses a least to most prompt for this skill. After Nick washes his hands, Jessie will gesture to the towel. If Nick does not respond, she gently moves his hand toward the towel. If Nick still doesn't respond, she will guide his hands to the towel to dry them off.

Example 3:

Nick has trouble putting the cover on the peanut butter jar when he is finished making a sandwich. Jessie uses a 2-second prompt delay to teach him. If he struggles with the cover for 2-seconds, she provides a physical prompt.

Describe/discuss this item.

Write more examples.

C – 08 IMPLEMENT STIMULUS CONTROL TRANSFER PROCEDURES.

(Supervisor only)

<u>Criteria</u>: *Role play*

<u>Assessment:</u>

- Roleplay a training session that requires a stimulus control transfer procedure according to the procedures used at your specific workplace. Require the technician to talk you through what he is doing as he is doing it. Please provide materials and a datasheet for the technician.

  REMEMBER: For this part of the assessment, the technician only needs to show competency with C-07 OR C-08 OR C-09 OR C-10, not all.

Notes:

Assessment notes:

Notes:

C – 09 IMPLEMENT STIMULUS FADING PROCEDURES.

Why is this important?

Stimulus fading is another way to teach responses. Usually there is some part of the material used that is highlighted or exaggerated to make the client more likely to select the target response. It can be highly effective because the response we want is likely to occur. (Hey, that sounds like prompt fading, right?) We can take advantage of our technique to reinforce the response when it occurs.

That explanation may a bit too technical. Stimulus fading is best described with examples. See below.

Example 1:

Jamie, an RBT, works with Dylan, a 3-year-old with difficulties around drinking liquids other than chocolate milk. Jamie's supervisor suggested a stimulus fading procedure to slowly and systematically get Dylan to drink regular milk. They decided to start with chocolate milk and slowly decrease the amount of chocolate added to the milk over the next two weeks.

Example 2:

Timmy has a new game on his iPad that teaches sight words. The app was designed using stimulus fading. When a new word is being taught, the answer is highlighted with a strong glow. Each time the word shows up as an answer on the app, the glow slowly disappears until eventually Timmy answers the question correctly on his own.

Example 3:

Tyra is an RBT at an elementary school. She often works on teaching kindergartners to cut on a line during art class. The materials are arranged so that when students start cutting, the lines they need to cut are about 2 inches thick. This allows the student to cut along the line. As the student gets better the lines on the materials get thinner and thinner until at some point the student is cutting the materials independently with a regular line.

Describe/discuss this item.

Write more examples.

C – 09 IMPLEMENT STIMULUS FADING PROCEDURES.

(Supervisor only)

Criteria: *Role play*

Assessment:

- Roleplay a training session that requires a stimulus fading procedure according to the procedures used at your specific workplace. Require the technician to talk you through what he is doing as he is doing it. Please provide materials and a datasheet for the technician.

  REMEMBER: For this part of the assessment, the technician only needs to show competency with C-07 OR C-08 OR C-09 OR C-10, not all.

Notes:

Assessment notes:

Notes:

C – 10 IMPLEMENT PROMPT AND PROMPT FADING PROCEDURES

Definition:

Prompts – "…antecedent stimuli that increase the probability of a desired response" (Fisher, Piazza, & Roane, 2013, p. 256).

Why is this important?

Prompting is an important part of teaching new skills. We prompt to make it more likely that our client engages in the correct response and therefore is more likely to access reinforcement. Then, we fade out our prompt so that they can be independent with whatever skill we are teaching. It is important to do because if we did not prompt initially, the response we attempted to teach may never have occurred.

We can split prompts into two different categories: response prompts and stimulus prompts.

Response prompts include:
- Verbal prompts
- Physical prompts
- Model prompts

Stimulus prompts include:
- Gestural prompts
- Positional prompts
- Within-stimulus prompts

Once prompts are implemented and the desired response is occurring, the next step is to fade the prompt. This is an important process to go through slowly and systematically. If we fade the prompt too quickly, the response may stop occurring. If we fade too slowly, the client may be relying on us longer than needed. The goal is to fade out the prompt with the right timing for the learner to be independent with that newly acquired skill.

Example 1:

Martha's son, Joshua, gets ABA services at home 4 hours a week. The RBT comes to her house to work on social skills. Martha has always been disappointed that Joshua will not play board games with his sister. He often complains that the games she picks are "too confusing". The RBT has been doing some parent training with Martha on how to deliver and fade out gestural prompts when Joshua is learning a new game. At first, Martha gave Joshua full gestural prompts about which card to pick up and when to lay a card down. Eventually she was able to fade out the prompts by barely making a movement toward the cards. After just a week of prompt fading, Joshua was playing a full game of cards with his sister.

Example 2:

Seth coached a tee ball team and wanted to make sure that each of his players had the opportunity to hit the ball. They often missed the ball even when it was on the tee. He decided to physically prompt them after two unsuccessful swings. To prompt, he stood behind them, using hand over hand guidance. By the end of the year, most of the players were independently hitting off the tee. Nice work, Coach Seth.

Describe/discuss this item.

Write more examples.

C – 10 IMPLEMENT PROMPT AND PROMPT FADING PROCEDURES

(Supervisor only)

<u>Criteria</u>: *Role play*

<u>Assessment</u>:

- Roleplay a training session that requires a prompting procedure according to the procedures used at your specific workplace. Require the technician to talk you through what he is doing as he is doing it. Please provide materials and a datasheet for the technician if needed.

- Roleplay how prompts are faded according to the procedures used at your specific workplace. Please provide materials and a datasheet for the technician if needed.

REMEMBER: For this part of the assessment, the technician only needs to show competency with C-07 OR C-08 OR C-09 OR C-10, not all.

Notes:

Assessment notes:

Notes:

Segment 6 – Scorecard
Skill Acquisition IV

(Supervisor checks boxes)

☐ Individual Supervision
☐ Group Supervision

C 11
☐ Assessment
☐ Workbook boxes completed

C 12
☐ Assessment
☐ Workbook boxes completed

Segment 6 – Individual Supervision Agenda

Supervisor: _____ **Technician:** _____

Meeting Date: _____ **Time of meeting – From:**_____ **To:**_____

This document covers supervisory period from ____/____/____ **to** ____/____/____

1. Review Workbook Boxes:

 Has supervisee satisfactorily completed workbook boxes?   Yes / No

- If not, what is needed to complete boxes? Describe below

2. Task List items addressed (C 11-12)

| |
| |
| |

3. Describe/Discuss task list items with technician

| |
| |
| |

4. Discussion topics or activities completed during this meeting:

Evaluation of Technician's Performance				
(Record: S- "Satisfactory"; NI- "Needs Improvement"; U- "Unsatisfactory"; or NA- "Not Applicable")				
Arrived on time for meeting		Gave examples as needed		
Completed workbook boxes		Accepted supervisory feedback appropriately		
Referred to task list item		Answered all questions thoroughly		
Maintained professional communication during supervision meeting				
Overall evaluation of supervisee performance during this meeting *(Circle one—use code above)*			S NI U	
If "NI" or "U", please list corrective steps needed to achieve a score of "S"				

5. Practice assigned for next meeting

| |
| |
| |

6. Closing questions/feedback

| |
| |
| |

Segment 6 – Group Supervision Meeting Agenda

- <u>Meeting Topic</u>: Skill Acquisition IV

- <u>Task List Items Reviewed</u>:
- C-11 Describe how to implement generalization and maintenance procedures.
- C-12 Explain how to assist with the training of stakeholders (e.g., family, caregivers, other professionals).

1. Housekeeping
   - Take attendance.
   - State the duration of today's meeting.
2. Task List Lesson and Discussion
   - Discuss task list item C-11 Describe how to implement generalization and maintenance procedures.
   - Discuss task list item C-12 Explain how to assist with the training of stakeholders (e.g., family, caregivers, other professionals).
3. Segment Review
   - Review segment items from current meeting
   - Review workbook boxes from RBTs to generate discussion
   - When presenting material, use response cards and ask frequent questions (raise hand, write on a paper and hold up the answer, etc.)
   - Use behavioral skills training to keep information interactive.
   - Include role play at every group meeting and do not rely on lecture for the bulk of meeting.
   - Raise specific case examples. Provide enough context for others in group to understand the idiosyncrasies of case. Do not dominate the time by discussing one or a handful of clients. Cover enough material to engage all learners and evoke behavior from RBTs.
4. Questions
   - Answer any relevant questions.
   - If RBTs do not ask have questions, quiz them on what you have covered in the meeting.
5. Closing Notes
   - Reinforce writing in workbook boxes and preparation for assessment.
   - Close the meeting by inviting supervisees to request topics to be covered in upcoming meetings.

C – 11 DESCRIBE HOW TO IMPLEMENT GENERALIZATION AND MAINTENANCE PROCEDURES

Definition:

Generalization – The effects of reinforcement beyond contexts in which reinforcement occurred.

Why is this important?

Generalization is important because when we teach a skill to a client, we often want this skill to occur in more than just our training session. If we teach washing hands, we don't want to have to teach it in every sink that the person comes across. We want generalization to occur so that person can wash his hands on any sink – whether it is a white porcelain sink or a stainless steel one.

In 1977, Stokes and Baer wrote an article about generalization that gives us some tips as below.

Tips to promote generalization:

- Introduce natural contingencies
- Train using many examples
- Use common stimuli when training
- Train loosely

Once we see generalization in a number of different settings, across several people, and/or with various different stimuli, we will want to make sure this newly learned skill maintains in these new environments.

When we speak of maintenance, we are talking about the sustained performance at a high level across time. This is important because if a client is taught a skill, but it is not maintained, it will probably have to be taught again in the future. That is inefficient and can take away from the opportunity to learn new skills. We can make sure that a skill is maintained by practicing the skill on consistent intervals. You might think about setting aside mastered programs to be run once every week or two.

Another way to make sure a skill is maintained is to embed the skill in new teaching procedures or activities. For instance, if your client mastered colors, you may want to include a game like UNO that requires the use of colors.

It could also be important to remind parents, teachers and caretakers to practice the mastered skills whenever they can.

Example 1:

Arun is an RBT and he works at a school for individuals diagnosed with autism. He has been working with Matthew, his student, on responding to greetings. Matthew learned to respond to a wave in his classroom at his work desk. Arun knows that just because Matthew waves at his work desk doesn't mean he will wave in the cafeteria or on the playground. Arun then moves the training into a variety of settings. This will promote generalization to occur in other places in the community and at home.

Example 2:

Arun programs opportunities for Matthew to practice responding when someone says "Hi Matthew" without a wave, with a wave, or when they just say, "Hi." Matthew now responds to many types of greetings in a variety of settings.

Example 3

Arun has been dedicated to teaching Matthew to respond to greetings in a variety of settings and with several variations. He is not going to allow Matthew to forget this. He programs maintenance trials every week and tells Matthew's parents to work on it at home and in the community.

Describe/discuss this item.

Write more examples.

C – 11 DESCRIBE HOW TO IMPLEMENT GENERALIZATION AND MAINTENANCE PROCEDURES

(Supervisor only)

<u>Criteria</u>: *Interview*

<u>Assessment</u>:
- Ask technician to define "generalization".
- Ask technician to describe why getting skills to generalize is important.
- Ask technician to give examples of some skills we would want to see generalize to a variety of stimulus arrangements.
- Ask technician to describe what is required by an RBT at your workplace to run maintenance procedures.

Notes:

Assessment notes:

Notes:

C – 12 EXPLAIN HOW TO ASSIST WITH THE TRAINING OF STAKEHOLDERS (E.G., FAMILY, CAREGIVERS, OTHER PROFESSIONALS).

Why is this important?
We hope to *teach* behavior we want to increase and *manage* behavior we want to decrease. If we can do this, we should share our process with everyone who interacts with our client.

We encourage you to demonstrate patience and professionalism when working with stakeholders. They may not know the science as well as you but they often know the client better because they have spent so much time together and tried different approaches to get behavior under control.

Each workplace will handle caregiver training differently. Some will want you to train the caregivers on the same methods you use during your session. Some places will be looking to the BCBA to handle those trainings.

If you are in a workplace that requires the RBT to train the caregivers, use a BST (behavioral skills training) model with caregivers. Talk to your supervisor in depth about what that is. Below is a very basic overview of BST.

Basic steps of BST:
1. Identify and provide rationale for why target skills are to be trained
2. Model the behavior for him/her to see
3. Have that person try it while you watch
4. Provide feedback on performance. Praise the things you liked and give one piece of advice to do it better next time.

Example 1:
Monica is the mother of James, a 4-year-old with autism. She has an RBT come to the home each day in the afternoon to teach communication and play skills. They are currently working on teaching PECS. During the session, the RBT said "Ok, we're going to work on teaching Phase 1 of PECS now. This is going to teach him to hand over the symbol. I'll be prompting him to hand it over and then we'll give him this cracker." The RBT then showed Monica how to do it. The RBT said "Do you mind trying the next one?". Monica

prompted the response and then stopped and said "Nice, James!"

The RBT said "Monica, wow! Nice prompt. Looks like he is starting to get the hang of it. One thing to do next time is make sure you hand over the cracker immediately after he hands you the icon. That way he learns that the handing it over will get him a cracker." Monica took the advice and did it perfectly the next time.

Example 2:
James often protested when Monica turned off the TV. At a recent meeting, the BCBA recommended to give a countdown from 10 to indicate that TV will be turned off. Now the RBT was assisting the mother in implementing that procedure.

The RBT said, "Monica, I'm glad you brought up the issue about the TV yesterday in the meeting. I've been seeing the same problem. Let's give the new procedure a try."

The RBT read the protocol the BCBA had sent and said, "OK, let's do it." The RBT gave the countdown and then turned the TV off. James cried for about 30 seconds. About 10 minutes later, James had earned enough tokens to get TV again. The RBT asked Monica if she would give the TV protocol a try this time. She did it. The RBT told Monica that she had done it correctly and not to worry about James crying for now. After all, the procedure may take a few days before an effect could be seen.

Describe/ discuss this item.

Write more examples.

C – 12 EXPLAIN HOW TO ASSIST WITH THE TRAINING OF STAKEHOLDERS (E.G., FAMILY, CAREGIVERS, OTHER PROFESSIONALS).

(Supervisor only)

Criteria: *Interview*
(TrainABA recommends a roleplay for C-12 but it is not required to pass the assessment)

Assessment:
- Ask your technician to describe why it is important to be patient and professional when interacting with stakeholders
- Ask your technician to describe how he would train a parent to teach a skill according to the procedures used in your workplace.
- Optional- Role play a caretaker training session

Notes:

Assessment notes:

Notes:

Segment 7 – Scorecard
Behavior Reduction

(Supervisor checks boxes)

☐ Individual Supervision
☐ Group Supervision

D 1
☐ Assessment
☐ Workbook boxes completed

D 4
☐ Assessment
☐ Workbook boxes completed

D 3
☐ Assessment
☐ Workbook boxes completed

D 5
☐ Assessment
☐ Workbook boxes completed

Segment 7 – Individual Supervision Agenda

Supervisor: _____ **Technician:** _____

Meeting Date: _____ **Time of meeting – From:**_____ **To:**_____

This document covers supervisory period from ____/____/____ to ____/____/____

1. Review Workbook Boxes:

    Has supervisee satisfactorily completed workbook boxes?   Yes / No

- If not, what is needed to complete boxes? Describe below

2. Task List items addressed (D 1; 3-5)

3. Describe/Discuss task list items with technician

4. Discussion topics or activities completed during this meeting:

Evaluation of Technician's Performance				
(Record: S- "Satisfactory"; NI- "Needs Improvement"; U- "Unsatisfactory"; or NA- "Not Applicable")				
Arrived on time for meeting		Gave examples as needed		
Completed workbook boxes		Accepted supervisory feedback appropriately		
Referred to task list item		Answered all questions thoroughly		
Maintained professional communication during supervision meeting				
Overall evaluation of supervisee performance during this meeting *(Circle one—use code above)*			S NI U	
If "NI" or "U", please list corrective steps needed to achieve a score of "S"				

5. Practice assigned for next meeting

6. Closing questions/feedback

Segment 7 – Group Supervision Meeting Agenda

- <u>Meeting Topic</u>: Behavior Reduction

- <u>Task List Items Reviewed</u>:
- D-01 Identify the essential components of a written behavior reduction plan.
- D-03 Implement interventions based on modification of antecedents such as motivating/establishing operations and discriminative stimuli.
- D-04 Implement differential reinforcement procedures (e.g., DRA, DRO).
- D-05 Implement extinction procedures.

1. Housekeeping
   - Take attendance.
   - State the duration of today's meeting.
2. Task List Lesson and Discussion
   - Discuss task list item D-01 Identify the essential components of a written behavior reduction plan.
   - Discuss task list item D-03 Implement interventions based on modification of antecedents such as motivating/establishing operations and discriminative stimuli.
   - Discuss task list item D-04 Implement differential reinforcement procedures (e.g., DRA, DRO).
   - Discuss task list item D-05 Implement extinction procedures.
3. Segment Review
   - Review segment items from current meeting
   - Review workbook boxes from RBTs to generate discussion
   - When presenting material, use response cards and ask frequent questions (raise hand, write on a paper and hold up the answer, etc.)
   - Use behavioral skills training to keep information interactive.
   - Include role play at every group meeting and do not rely on lecture for the bulk of meeting.
   - Raise specific case examples. Provide enough context for others in group to understand the idiosyncrasies of case. Do not dominate the time by discussing one or a handful of clients. Cover enough material to engage all learners and evoke behavior from RBTs.
4. Questions
   - Answer any relevant questions.
   - If RBTs do not ask have questions, quiz them on what you have covered in the meeting.
5. Closing Notes
   - Reinforce writing in workbook boxes and preparation for assessment.
   - Close the meeting by inviting supervisees to request topics to be covered in upcoming meetings.

D – 01 IDENTIFY THE ESSENTIAL COMPONENTS OF A BEHAVIOR REDUCTION PLAN.

Why is this important?

A behavior reduction plan is a document that contains information for understanding a client's behavior. It helps everyone working with the client to use a consistent approach for reducing problem behavior.

The BCBA supervisor will write these plans based on his understanding of the problem behavior and assessments he's conducted. There are many different treatments that could be used but (lucky for you) only the supervisor has to do that part. Your job, as an RBT, is to run the program as written (even if you think it is terrible) and be a good observer and recorder of behavior. Components of a behavior reduction plan vary widely from workplace to workplace but there are many components that will be found in a majority of plans.

Here are a few commonly seen components of a behavior reduction plan:
- Target behavior definitions
- Contexts that the target behavior is likely to occur
- Data collection methods described
- Treatment description – what to do before, during, and after the response occurs
- Emergency procedures

For examples of a behavior reduction plan at your workplace, ask your supervisor to review the components with you.

Describe/ discuss this item.

Write more examples.

D – 01 IDENTIFY THE ESSENTIAL COMPONENTS OF A BEHAVIOR REDUCTION PLAN.

(Supervisor only)

Criteria: *Interview*

Assessment:

- Without having a behavior reduction plan in his hand, ask the technician to describe the essential components of a behavior reduction plan at your workplace.
- With a behavior reduction plan available, ask the technician to point out the various components of the plan and describe how each component is useful.

Notes:

Assessment notes:

NOTES:

D – 03 IMPLEMENT INTERVENTIONS BASED ON MODIFICATION OF ANTECEDENTS SUCH AS MOTIVATING/ESTABLISHING OPERATIONS AND DISCRIMINATIVE STIMULI.

Handwritten note: An-te-sid-dent. A thing or event that existed before or logically.

Handwritten note: manipulate. arrange the environment to make your item more valuable.

Definitions:

Antecedent – "An environmental condition or stimulus change existing or occurring prior to a behavior of interest." (Cooper, Heron, & Heward, 2007, p.689)

Motivating operations – an environmental variable that changes the value of a stimulus and changes the frequency of a response.

Discriminative stimuli – "A stimulus in the presence of which responses of some type have been reinforced and in the absence of which the same type of responses have occurred and not been reinforced." (Cooper, Heron, & Heward, 2007, p. 694)

Why is this important?

Antecedent interventions are those that we make before a response occurs. We can make changes to the environment so certain responses are more likely and others are less likely.

The antecedent changes we make usually fall into two categories:

1. Motivating operations - We would manipulate the motivating operations to make a particular reinforcer more or less valuable, therefore making the target response more or less likely. A manipulation that is made to make a reinforcer more valuable is considered an **establishing operation.**

2. Discriminative stimuli – We often try to make things clearer to our clients. We will make changes to the stimuli they are contacting to show them which responses may be reinforced and which ones may not be reinforced. This type of manipulation is related to **discriminative stimuli.**

Example 1 - Motivating operation

Chase, an RBT, is working on teaching Mary, a 12-year-old diagnosed with autism, to request water when she wants it. One of the ways that Chase has arranged the environment to make water more valuable is to play chase outside in the summer sun for 10 minutes before he gets the water out so she can practice requesting. Smart move, Chase.

Example 2 – Discriminative stimuli

Jade is an RBT that works with Steven, a 35-year-old at a group home. Steven will often forget to brush his teeth in the evening. Jade worked with Steven to create a routine checklist that Steven will go through each evening before going to bed. Steven passes the checklist into Jade before he goes to bed. Steven remembers to complete the entire routine now without prompting.

Handwritten note: vision board.

Describe/ discuss this item.

Write more examples.

D – 03 IMPLEMENT INTERVENTIONS BASED ON MODIFICATION OF ANTE-CEDENTS SUCH AS MOTIVATING/ESTAB-LISHING OPERATIONS AND DISCRIMI-NATIVE STIMULI.

(Supervisor only)

<u>Criteria</u>: *Role play*

<u>Assessment:</u>

- Roleplay a training session that requires a modification of motivating operations that you may use at your workplace. It would be best if the technician was able to come up with the situation on his own.
- Roleplay a training session that requires a modification of discriminative stimuli that you may use at your workplace. It would be best if the technician was able to come up with the situation on his own.

REMEMBER: For this part of the assess-ment, the technician only needs to show competency with D-03 OR D-04 OR D-05, not all.

Notes:

Assessment notes:

Notes:

D – 04 IMPLEMENT DIFFERENTIAL REINFORCEMENT PROCEDURES (E.G., DRA, DRO)

Definition:
Differential reinforcement of alternative behavior (DRA) – "A procedure for decreasing problem behavior in which reinforcement is delivered for a behavior that serves as a desirable alternative to the behavior targeted for reduction and withheld following instances of the problem behavior" (Cooper, Heron, & Heward, 2007, p 693).

Differential reinforcement of other behavior (DRO) – "A procedure for decreasing problem behavior in which reinforcement is contingent on the absence of the problem behavior during or at specific times" (Cooper, Heron, & Heward, 2007, p 694).

Why is this important?
DRA and DRO are commonly used procedures to decrease problem behavior.

DRA is a way to have someone engage in an appropriate response to get access to something they want instead of engaging in problem behavior.

DRO gives individuals a high preference item/activity after a certain period of time without problem behavior. We reinforce all behavior except for the problematic response.

Example - DRA:
give the item until they give an appropriate response.

Johnny tantrums when prompted to do his homework, falling on the ground screaming. Johnny's mom asked the BCBA supervisor what could be done about this behavior. The supervisor suggested a DRA procedure to teach Johnny to ask for a break when he does not want to do his homework. His homework needs to get done each night so the BCBA also suggested that TV and snacks be withheld until Johnny completes all of his homework.

Example - DRO:
Max is an RBT who works with Jenna, a 7-year-old girl with autism. Jenna engages in hand mouthing behavior and is starting to get some sores on her mouth. The BCBA supervisor wrote a behavior reduction plan and included a DRO. As written, Max gives Jenna a small piece of fruit each time Jenna goes 5 minutes without hand mouthing. To get the fruit, it does not matter what Jenna is doing as long as she is not handmouthing. If she does engage in handmouthing, she does not get the piece of fruit that interval but has a chance to get it in the next 5-minute period.

Give the reward everytime the patient stops doing their stimulus on certain times. Smin 10 min-

Describe/discuss this item.

Write more examples.

D – 04 IMPLEMENT DIFFERENTIAL REIN-FORCEMENT PROCEDURES (E.G., DRA, DRO)

(Supervisor only)

<u>Criteria</u>: *Role play*

<u>Assessment:</u>

- Roleplay a DRA procedure that you may use at your workplace. It would be best if the technician was able to come up with the situation on her own. Focus on making sure that the alternative response will replace the problematic behavior based on function.

- Roleplay a DRO procedure that you may use at your workplace. It would be best if the technician was able to come up with the situation on her own.

    REMEMBER: For this part of the assessment, the technician only needs to show competency with D-03 OR D-04 OR D-05, not all.

Notes:

Assessment notes:

Notes:

D – 05 IMPLEMENT EXTINCTION PROCEDURES.

Definition:

Extinction - "The discontinuing of a reinforcement of a previously reinforced behavior (i.e., responses no longer produce reinforcement)" (Cooper, Heron, & Heward, 2007, p. 695).

Why is this important?

Extinction procedures are often the simplest and most common procedures to understand in ABA. This being said, it is not always easily implemented.

Extinction relies on the discontinuation of a schedule of reinforcement. That means that if *attention* was reinforcing some problem behavior, then we would no longer give it attention. If the removal of some aversive situation is reinforcing some problem behavior, then we would no longer give it escape.

This may make it easier: *achin by kiddo*

- If a response is for attention, we do not deliver attention contingent on problem behavior.
- If a response is for escape, we do not deliver escape contingent on problem behavior.
- If a response is to get tangible items, we do not deliver tangible items contingent on problem behavior.

Many times extinction is difficult to implement because an individual's behavior is too severe to ignore or he/she is too big to prompt through the aversive situation.

It is recommended to use reinforcement based procedures (DRA) to supplement the use of extinction. *Differential reinforcement of Alternative.*

Example 1:

Sameh is an RBT and he's working with Frank, a 4-year-old with autism. The BCBA reports that Frank's parents often give him his toys whenever he starts to scream to calm him down. Sameh uses an extinction procedure for the screaming. He withholds toys when Frank screams.

Withhold items during the stimulus or inappropriate behavior

Example 2:

Michelle is an RBT who works with Tamika, a 17-year-old in a group home. Each night after Michelle puts Tamika to bed, she will come out and ask Michelle to play a game of peekaboo with her. At first, Michelle did not mind because she thought it was cute. After almost two weeks, the cuteness wore off because Tamika was not sleeping enough and displaying more behavioral outbursts during the day.

The BCBA supervisor advised Michelle to use an extinction procedure at night time. Michelle told Tamika, "I am not going to play peekaboo at bed time any more." She ignored Tamika and told her to go back to bed. Tamika protested with crying and physical aggression the first night but eventually went back to bed.

Describe/ discuss this item.

Write more examples.

D – 05 IMPLEMENT EXTINCTION PROCE-DURES.

(Supervisor only)

<u>Criteria</u>: *Role play*

<u>Assessment:</u>

- Roleplay an extinction procedure for a response you may see at your workplace. It would be best if the technician was able to come up with the situation on her own. Make sure that the reinforcer is identified for the role play so the extinction procedure is based on the correct function.

  REMEMBER: For this part of the assessment, the technician only needs to show competency with D-03 OR D-04 OR D-05, not all.

Notes:

Assessment notes:

Notes:

Segment 8 – Scorecard Documentation and Reporting

(Supervisor checks boxes)

☐ Individual Supervision
☐ Group Supervision

D 6
☐ Assessment
☐ Workbook boxes completed

E 1
☐ Assessment
☐ Workbook boxes completed

E 2
☐ Assessment
☐ Workbook boxes completed

Segment 8 – Individual Supervision Agenda

Supervisor: _____ **Technician:** _____

Meeting Date: _____ **Time of meeting – From:**_____ **To:**_____

This document covers supervisory period from ____/____/____ **to** ____/____/____

1. Review Workbook Boxes:

    Has supervisee satisfactorily completed workbook boxes?   Yes / No

- If not, what is needed to complete boxes? Describe below

2. Task List items addressed (D 6; E 1-2)

3. Describe/Discuss task list items with technician

4. Discussion topics or activities completed during this meeting:

Evaluation of Technician's Performance					
(Record: S- "Satisfactory"; NI- "Needs Improvement"; U- "Unsatisfactory"; or NA- "Not Applicable")					
Arrived on time for meeting		Gave examples as needed			
Completed workbook boxes		Accepted supervisory feedback appropriately			
Referred to task list item		Answered all questions thoroughly			
Maintained professional communication during supervision meeting					
Overall evaluation of supervisee performance during this meeting *(Circle one—use code above)*			S	NI	U
If "NI" or "U", please list corrective steps needed to achieve a score of "S"					

5. Practice assigned for next meeting

6. Closing questions/feedback

Segment 8 – Group Supervision Meeting Agenda

- <u>Meeting Topic</u>: Documentation and Reporting

- <u>Task List Items Reviewed</u>:

- D-06 Implement crisis/emergency procedures according to protocol.
- E-01 Report other variables that might affect the client (e.g., illness, relocation, medication).
- E-02 Generate objective session notes by describing what occurred during sessions.

1. Housekeeping
   - Take attendance.
   - State the duration of today's meeting.
2. Task List Lesson and Discussion
   - Discuss task list item D-06 Implement crisis/emergency procedures according to protocol.
   - Discuss task list item E-01 Report other variables that might affect the client (e.g., illness, relocation, medication).
   - Discuss task list item E-02 Generate objective session notes by describing what occurred during sessions.
3. Segment Review
   - Review segment items from current meeting
   - Review workbook boxes from RBTs to generate discussion
   - When presenting material, use response cards and ask frequent questions (raise hand, write on a paper and hold up the answer, etc.)
   - Use behavioral skills training to keep information interactive.
   - Include role play at every group meeting and do not rely on lecture for the bulk of meeting.
   - Raise specific case examples. Provide enough context for others in group to understand the idiosyncrasies of case. Do not dominate the time by discussing one or a handful of clients. Cover enough material to engage all learners and evoke behavior from RBTs.
4. Questions
   - Answer any relevant questions.
   - If RBTs do not ask have questions, quiz them on what you have covered in the meeting.
5. Closing Notes
   - Reinforce writing in workbook boxes and preparation for assessment.
   - Close the meeting by inviting supervisees to request topics to be covered in upcoming meetings.

D – 06 IMPLEMENT CRISIS/EMERGENCY PROCEDURES ACCORDING TO PROTOCOL.

What is it?

Emergency procedures for times of crisis are a part of every well written behavior plan. We write them in hopes that we never have to use them but we practice them because an emergency may happen.

The best way to prepare for an emergency is to have a plan that is written down and reviewed at specific times during the year. We should practice the skills required of us so that we are fluent in the skills when we need them.

Plans can be written for any type of emergency but there are common types of emergencies in our field.

- Extreme episodes of problem behavior in the home – self-injury, aggression and property destruction
- Extreme episodes of problem behavior in the community – self-injury, aggression and property destruction
- Missing client – elopement or AWOL
- Medical emergencies – first aid training
- Fire escape

Example 1:

Jack is a client at a residential facility. He is 15 years old and elopes from the residence daily. The residential facility has alarmed doors in case clients leave the building without anyone noticing. That morning, one of the staff members realized that Jack was not in the residence and that someone had forgotten to turn the alarm on. The staff immediately followed the emergency guidelines, sending one staff to search for Jack, another staff to call supervisors. Within three minutes, Jack was found wandering in the neighbor's back yard.

Example 2:

Abdullah is a 10-year-old boy diagnosed with autism. He has difficulty in the community. Typically, he will engage in minor aggression at restaurants when waiting for his food to come. Staff tend to redirect him to his toys when that happens. Today, Abdullah started throwing plates off the table and hitting staff very hard with a closed fist. This was abnormal behavior but luckily the team had designed some emergency procedures for when this type of behavior occurred. Two staff escorted Abdullah out of the restaurant. The supervisor went to talk to the manager of the restaurant to apologize. Other staff kept everyone the other residential clients calm and actively engaged with games and toys. The plan was successful at minimizing damage and making sure everyone was safe.

Describe/ discuss this item.

Write more examples.

D – 06 IMPLEMENT CRISIS/EMERGENCY PROCEDURES ACCORDING TO PROTOCOL.

(Supervisor only)

<u>Criteria</u>: *Role play*

<u>Assessment:</u>
- Role play some of the emergency procedures used at your workplace. There are probably several to go through and discuss.

Notes:

Assessment notes:

Notes:

E – 01 REPORT OTHER VARIABLES THAT MIGHT AFFECT THE CLIENT (E.G., ILLNESS, RELOCATION, MEDICATION).

What is it?

Behavior analysis only works if we have the necessary data. Sometimes, behavioral interventions fail because the child has a fever or some other physical issue. A change in psychiatric medication often influences behavior. Physical and mental health play important roles in how clients respond to behavioral treatment. Things like moving to a new school or home could also make it difficult for clients to make behavioral progress. If a supervisor knows about these variables, she or he can make better decisions. You are the eyes and ears of the supervisor. Be sure to report other variables that might affect the client's behavioral progress, especially illness, relocation, and medication-related issues.

Example:

Susie, an experienced RBT™, looked at her phone while walking into a session. Tina, her BCBA® supervisor, texted, "Hey lady, great team meeting yesterday. Let me know how Bobbie-Jaye does with the toileting program." Susie texted back, "Hey Tina, I'm on it. Stay tuned." She started working with Bobbie-Jaye.

What a horrible session. It was almost like no matter what Susie tried – bubbles, iPad, hiding under the blanket – Bobbie-Jaye indicated no interest. He was staring at the wall with a blank expression on his face. Susie wondered what the heck was going on with this little guy. He was usually one of her most responsive clients. At age 5, it was time to get him out of diapers in hopes that he could join the mainstream kindergarten program next September. The toilet training program was crucial. But Bobbie was unresponsive.

Susie texted her supervisor. "Tina, nothing is working. He keeps staring blankly at the wall, saying he doesn't feel good." Tina texted back, "Staring? WTF?" (Susie knew that Tina often abbreviated "what's the function" by typing WTF.) Tina wrote back, "He's not escaping anything by staring. Not getting extra attention. Not accessing tangibles. I don't know. Any guesses? WTF?" Tina replied, "Ask mom if the doctor changed his meds."

Susie asked Bobbie-Jaye's mother if she knew what might be happening. His mother said that

Bobbie-Jaye's psychiatrist prescribed an anti-depressant recently and that symptoms could include depressive symptoms for the first couple of weeks before improvement would be seen. "The doctor said it was like, 'one step back to take two steps forward.'" Susie thanked her for sharing that information.

When Tina received the update, she was glad to see an explanation that made sense. She thanked Susie for reporting the other variables that might have affected Bobbie-Jaye's behavioral progress. She told Susie to put the toileting program on hold until Bobbie-Jaye's doctor said he no longer showed depressive symptoms. "It's a good thing we knew about the medication change," Tina told Susie, "Otherwise, we might have thought the toileting program was ineffective and we would have tried something more restrictive."

Susie thought about Tina's comment when she went home that night. It seemed like her clients received so many services – psychiatrists, physical therapists, speech-language pathologists, counselors, and the ABA team. Many of the clients followed restricted diets. It was like their parents were trying whatever they could afford to see if it helped. Susie made it a point to write other variables like illness and medication in the session notes going forward. She made a list of factors that could be a big deal in a client's life:

1. Illness
2. Medication change
3. Moving to a new home
4. Change of bus/transportation schedule
5. Starting a new school
6. Gaining a new sibling
7. Starting puberty
8. Eating a special diet
9. Being in a warm or cold room without air conditioning or heat
10. Urinary tract infection
11. Dehydration
12. High energy client who is expected to sit in school and on the bus all day

There were many other factors worth reporting in the session notes of texting to her supervisor. Susie saw how important it was to report those variables.

Describe/ discuss this item.

Write more examples.

E – 01 REPORT OTHER VARIABLES THAT MIGHT AFFECT THE CLIENT (E.G., ILLNESS, RELOCATION, MEDICATION).

(Supervisor only)

<u>Criteria</u>: *Interview*

<u>Assessment:</u>

- Ask technician to discuss why it was important for Susie's supervisor to know about Bobbie-Jaye's medication in the above example.
- Choose one item from the list of 12 factors listed above and ask technician to describe/discuss why that variable matters and how it should be reported.
- Ask technician to describe how she or he would go about report other variables that might affect the client (e.g., who to tell, where to write it, when to report it).
- Think of a client on the technician's caseload. Ask the technician what other variables might have affected that client's behavioral progress in the last year.
- At a live observation, ask technician to show you what she or he would do if the client showed signs of illness worth reporting (e.g., write in section of program book, verify information, contact supervisor, terminate or continue session, etc.).
- Ask technician to describe the company illness policy for cancelled sessions. Verify the answer with a company human resources professional.

Notes:

Assessment notes:

Notes:

E – 02 GENERATE OBJECTIVE SESSION NOTES BY DESCRIBING WHAT OCCURRED DURING SESSIONS.

What is it?

Objective session notes answer questions like what, when, who, how, and where. They do not explain *why* behavior occurred. They state facts, not opinions. Objective session notes convey a message of factual events with enough context or background to understand what happened before or after an important behavioral event. Do not state your interpretation of what those events might mean. When in doubt, write notes recording what a camera and microphone could record and declare inferences.

Why does this matter?

Objective session notes are data. Your supervisor uses the information from session notes when making programming decisions and writing reports to send to parents, schools, and funding sources. Stating observed events is useful to people who were not there to see or hear it.

Examples:

"Jacob was tired today so he did not do very well."
How does the author know Billy was tired? Were his eyes closing and did he fall asleep on break? The author could have written those things instead because a camera could see them. Why write, *"…so he did not do very well"*? Write that his scores were lower than average.

"Kalisha's brother took her toy and Kalisha got mad and hit him, super hard."
Guess who Ben just fired? Whoever wrote this awful session note. It started off objective with, "Kalisha's brother took her toy." That makes sense. A camera could see that. Then the note took a turn for the worst with, "Kalisha got mad and hit him." What's wrong with these notes? We do not know if Kalisha was mad. A camera does not know what emotions a person is experiencing. That is why they call it acting, right? It may look like Harry Potter was in a high-flying Quidditch match but really he was in front of a green screen in a Hollywood studio somewhere. If Kalisha said, "I'm so mad, I'm going to hit you," then we could have written her statement in the session notes.

The author also said Kalisha hit her brother, "super hard." The notes should have said something like, "Forcefully, on his right ear, and he did not bleed." That is more specific.

"Denzel had green mucus today and the thermometer showed a fever. He was unable to participate in programs after the first 20 minutes. Session only lasted 30 minutes. His mother said she would take him to the pharmacy after session to get medicine for his symptoms. I notified the office and supervisor of the change to schedule and reason for ending session early.
The session notes above were excellent. The writing is clear and to-the-point. There are no opinions. Everything important is stated. It does not leave the reader with questions. Everything makes sense.

"The teacher (Miguel O'Shaughnessy) told Melinda to hang up her coat and sit down for morning circle. Melinda was unresponsive. Teacher used hand-over-hand prompt to guide Melinda to hang up the coat, then directed her vocally to sit for morning circle. Melinda ran outside of the classroom through the side exit. She picked up a rock and threw it at the front door, cracking the glass. The paraprofessional, (Federico Steinwitzbergman) maintained a visual on Melinda at all times and used a verbal prompt for her to sit in her desk to calm herself with deep breathing. Melinda complied. The school office was notified to cover the cracked window with tape and cardboard for safety."
The above session note was a mock Special Incident Report (SIR) at a private school for special education. The note is objective, clear, and complete. There are no opinions, inferences, or assumptions on the reader's part. The author did not attempt to say why Melinda engaged in property destruction. The session note is well written.

"Alvin was playing with his younger brother when I arrived and began to tantrum when session started. However, I gave him a choice of reinforcers and he began working for coloring book. He scored higher than average in his task completion program today, achieving 80% for review and 90% on his new target, random rotated with known items. He had one tantrum for 15 minutes."
The above note is objective but perhaps too thorough. Unless specifically requested by a supervisor, the percentages and programming information for the task completion program is unnecessary. It is too specific for session notes at most companies. Supervisors have organized a program book to keep the percentages in the right places. The task completion tab is the place to find detailed percentages – not session notes.

Keep the session notes objective and general enough to convey the major events of the session. The part about playing with his younger brother and tantruming at the start of session was excellent.

Session notes are always objective and free from opinion. The notes should report on things a camera and microphone could detect. Enough context should be provided to clarify what happened. Check with your supervisor to see how session notes should be written at your company.

Describe/discuss this item.

Write more examples.

E – 02 GENERATE OBJECTIVE SESSION NOTES BY DESCRIBING WHAT OCCURRED DURING SESSIONS.

(Supervisor only)

<u>Criteria</u>: *Interview*

<u>Assessment</u>:
- Ask technician to describe the difference between objective and subjective session notes. Why do objective session notes only describe what occurred during sessions?
- Ask technician to provide examples of objective language for session notes.
- Ask technician to describe how she or he selected objective language in summary notes at a recent session.

Notes:

Assessment notes:

Notes:

Segment 9 – Scorecard Communication and Supervision

(Supervisor checks boxes)

☐ Individual Supervision
☐ Group Supervision

E 3
☐ Assessment
☐ Workbook boxes completed

F 3
☐ Assessment
☐ Workbook boxes completed

F 2
☐ Assessment
☐ Workbook boxes completed

Segment 9 – Individual Supervision Agenda

Supervisor: _____ **Technician:** _____

Meeting Date: _____ **Time of meeting – From:**_____ **To:**_____

This document covers supervisory period from ____/____/____ **to** ____/____/____

1. Review Workbook Boxes:

   Has supervisee satisfactorily completed workbook boxes?   Yes / No

   - If not, what is needed to complete boxes? Describe below

2. Task List items addressed (E 3; F 2-3)

3. Describe/Discuss task list items with technician

4. Discussion topics or activities completed during this meeting:

Evaluation of Technician's Performance			
(Record: S- "Satisfactory"; NI- "Needs Improvement"; U- "Unsatisfactory"; or NA- "Not Applicable")			
Arrived on time for meeting		Gave examples as needed	
Completed workbook boxes		Accepted supervisory feedback appropriately	
Referred to task list item		Answered all questions thoroughly	
Maintained professional communication during supervision meeting			
Overall evaluation of supervisee performance during this meeting *(Circle one—use code above)*			S NI U
If "NI" or "U", please list corrective steps needed to achieve a score of "S"			

5. Practice assigned for next meeting

6. Closing questions/feedback

Segment 9 – Group Supervision Meeting Agenda

- <u>Meeting Topic</u>: Communication and Supervision

- <u>Task List Items Reviewed</u>:
- E-03 Identify methods to effectively communicate with supervisor.
- F-02 Respond appropriately to feedback and maintain or improve performance accordingly.
- F-03 Explain how to communicate with stakeholders (e.g., family, caregivers, other professionals) as authorized.

1. Housekeeping
   - Take attendance.
   - State the duration of today's meeting.
2. Task List Lesson and Discussion
   - Discuss task list item E-03 Identify methods to effectively communicate with supervisor.
   - Discuss task list item F-02 Respond appropriately to feedback and maintain or improve performance accordingly.
   - Discuss task list item F-03 Explain how to communicate with stakeholders (e.g., family, caregivers, other professionals) as authorized.
3. Segment Review
   - Review segment items from current meeting
   - Review workbook boxes from RBTs to generate discussion
   - When presenting material, use response cards and ask frequent questions (raise hand, write on a paper and hold up the answer, etc.)
   - Use behavioral skills training to keep information interactive.
   - Include role play at every group meeting and do not rely on lecture for the bulk of meeting.
   - Raise specific case examples. Provide enough context for others in group to understand the idiosyncrasies of case. Do not dominate the time by discussing one or a handful of clients. Cover enough material to engage all learners and evoke behavior from RBTs.
4. Questions
   - Answer any relevant questions.
   - If RBTs do not ask have questions, quiz them on what you have covered in the meeting.
5. Closing Notes
   - Reinforce writing in workbook boxes and preparation for assessment.
   - Close the meeting by inviting supervisees to request topics to be covered in upcoming meetings.

E – 03 IDENTIFY METHODS TO EFFECTIVELY COMMUNICATE WITH SUPERVISOR.

What is it?

If you can believe it, supervisors have even more responsibilities than RBTs. Seemingly unimportant RBT™ behavior can adversely impact the program, leaving the supervisor in an ethical bind. Your actions as an RBT™ could threaten your supervisor's job and certification. Effective communication is the key to working together. Some key ideas are provided below.

When there is conflict at work:

Keep your content clear
Use a neutral tone
Use non-emotional phrasing

Communication methods:

Use the same professional tone, phrasing, and word choice on every communication platform – text messaging, email, phone, in person, and session notes.

Text messages – Used to reach people immediately. Respond as soon as possible. Keep it short and to-the-point. Do not use emotional language, humor, exclamation points, or abbreviations in texts.

Email – Used to communicate information that cannot fit in a text or should be shared with multiple people, usually other professionals or key stakeholders. Emails are kept in company archives and are often forwarded up the chain of command without your knowledge. Imagine that every email could be read by the CEO of the company. Do not use emotional language, humor, exclamation points, or abbreviations in email.

Phone – Used to have brief, real-time conversations about something important and often complicated. It is used to discuss complicated behavioral issues or to say things without leaving a permanent record. Keep your emotions in check at all times on the phone. You are only communicating what you say over telephone. Non-verbal communication is not heard over the phone. Confirm that you understood your supervisor and restate what you heard her tell you, using some of the exact words.

In-Person – At least twice per month, you will meet with your supervisor face-to-face. The majority of how you communicate in-person is not what you say. Things like tone of voice, eye contact, personal hygiene/appearance, personal odor, posture, facial expression, and the overall mood you convey are communicated in-person. The words you choose play a small role in the overall communication exchange. Be mindful that you do not want to appear disheveled, overwhelmed, tired, angry, frustrated, etc. Use in-person communication to display human elements appropriate for work – appreciation and gratitude, compassion and empathy, excitement and passion – and to empower others. You can deliver social reinforcement more effectively and immediately in-person than other forms of communication.

General Tips:

Try to see things from your supervisor's perspective, having empathy. Supervisors generally manage a high volume of tasks and responsibilities on tight deadlines. They appreciate the same kind of communication that you would use for session notes:
Provide the facts.
Treat the situation with respect.
Use a neutral tone with objective language.
Use a non-emotional phrasing.

Treat situations with respect even when you think it may be unimportant. Some things may appear trivial to a technician but may be extremely important to the behavioral program or BCBA®. The reports, programs, and data collection may be required legally for IEPs at school, insurance plans at home, etc.

Example:

A technician wondered why the supervisor cared about tracking AWOL. The child had not engaged in the behavior since the RBT™ started working with him three months ago. The technician stopped collecting data. The supervisor gave her feedback, saying it was crucial to record data on all the problem behaviors. "It is part of the Free and Appropriate Public Education legal requirement," said the supervisor. "There is always a reason for what I ask you to do."

General note:

Scheduling issues, vacations, sick days, gossip, and lateness, for example, could be major issues to a supervisor depending on the situation. Provide clear information in a neutral tone, exercising self-control in how you phrase things. Work is not the place for emotional discussions. Coworkers do not have time or training for that kind of communication.

Describe/discuss this item.

Write more examples.

E – 03 IDENTIFY METHODS TO EFFECTIVELY COMMUNICATE WITH SUPERVISOR.

(Supervisor only)

<u>Criteria</u>: *Interview*

<u>Assessment</u>:
- Ask technician to describe etiquette for communicating with supervisors over text, email, phone, and/or in-person.
- Ask technician how she or he would communicate a strongly-held emotional conviction to the supervisor.
- Ask technician to discuss and demonstrate communication with clear content, a neutral tone, and non-emotional phrasing.

Notes:

Assessment notes:

Notes:

F – 02 RESPOND APPROPRIATELY TO FEEDBACK AND MAINTAIN OR IMPROVE PERFORMANCE ACCORDINGLY.

What is it?
Feedback has 3 components:
1. Positive feedback
2. Corrective feedback
3. Follow-up

BACB® supervisors learn about feedback in the 8-Hour Supervisor Training, a pre-requisite to supervising RBTs.

Why is this important?
One of the most common reasons people leave companies is a poor relationship with their supervisors. Feedback is extremely important. It can make or break the tone of a person's day. Have you been a victim of one of these feedback *faux pas*? (See non-examples at right.)

Positive feedback uses contingent, descriptive praise.
Corrective feedback uses the 6–steps on the table in the Assessment section for this task list item.

Notes:

Non-examples:
- A short-tempered supervisor says, "You've been awful lately. Work on it." Awful at what? In what way? When? And what exactly am I supposed to improve? Feedback is meant to lead to behavioral change. A better phrasing could be, "Jayquan, you were late again to session today. That makes three times this week. What's getting in the way of being there on time?"
- At your annual performance review, you see a note from your supervisor saying you used inadvertent prompts frequently. It would have been more productive for your supervisor to practice the skill with you months ago rather than letting you do it wrong all this time.

Examples:
- A great supervisor said, "I notice you have the stimuli close together. Let me jump in for a few trials and show you what would look clearer." (Modeling is a form of feedback.)
- A supervisor says, "Jaechelle, I want you to collect data on how long it takes you to prepare for the session, from the minute you walk in the door to the minute you start running programs. It will help me know whether to reorganize the program book or give you extra training." (Self-monitored data is a form of feedback.)

Describe/discuss this item.

Write more examples.

F – 02 RESPOND APPROPRIATELY TO FEEDBACK AND MAINTAIN OR IMPROVE PERFORMANCE ACCORDINGLY.

(Supervisor only)

<u>Criteria</u>: *Observation (may include role play)*

<u>Assessment:</u>

- NOTE: the RBT Competency Assessment evaluates only the "respond appropriately to feedback" element.
- Choose a method of providing feedback to which technician responds.
  - o *Tip:* The BACB® allows you to role play this item but we advise against it. Feedback should be provided during individual supervision contacts monthly. Additional feedback opportunities may arise in the form of scheduled performance reviews, emails from RBT, etc.
  - o *For new technicians:* Provide feedback early in the relationship. Having a new technician is a common reason for assessing this item via role play yet the new relationship serves as a great excuse for the technician to practice responding to feedback.
- Using the BACB®'s 6-steps for Delivering Corrective Feedback table below, verify that technician responds appropriately to each step.

Delivering Corrective Feedback	
1. Provide an empathy statement	
2. Describe ineffective performance	
3. Provide a rationale for desired change in performance	
4. Provide instructions and demonstration for how to improve designated performance	
5. Provide opportunities to practice the desired performance	
6. Provide immediate feedback	

Notes:

Assessment notes:

Notes:

F – 03 EXPLAIN HOW TO COMMUNICATE WITH STAKEHOLDERS (E.G., FAMILY, CAREGIVERS, OTHER PROFESSIONALS) AS AUTHORIZED.

What is it?
Communication counts. Use a professional tone when communicating at work, remembering company policies and the BACB® Compliance Code.

Why is this important?
Great communication skills lead to job security, better performance reviews, and a more productive work environment.
Poor communication skills lead to sanctions, termination, and problems at work.

Example:
This is a true story. A highly verbal 8-year-old female client was working on conversation skills as part of her behavioral program. During the program, the technician was asked to provide enough information to simulate a real-life conversation. The little girl asked, "So how old are you?"
"I'm 28," said the technician.
"Are you married?" the little girl asked.
"No," the technician said.
"Do you have a boyfriend?" she asked.
"No," said the technician. She was wondering where the client was going with this line of questioning.
The little girl looked at her from head to toe with a judging stare. "Better get on that," she said. Is that a great example of how not to communicate, or what?
Let's reverse roles. When you work in a family's home or school, communication is important. Obviously, you do not want to say things that violate acceptable professional behavior, company policy, or the BACB® Compliance Code. In a program like what is listed above, the technician was authorized to share the amount of information she provided. Imagine if she started talking about her dating life, or lack thereof. It would have been inappropriate to share that much information at work. What if the technician took out her phone and scrolled through her Tinder account with the client, teaching her to swipe right on cute guys to see if they wrote back? Sharing too much personal information at work is a problem.
Communication is a two-way street. You have a powerful role in the lives of family members and caregivers for the clients you serve. Sharing some

basic, harmless information is generally appreciated because it makes you seem less like a clinician and more like a real person.

Another true story is about Gary, one of Ben's (author) first supervisors. Gary was hired as an interim clinical director. Ben and Gary drove around Los Angeles County to meet clients. As a new consultant, the young Ben prepared graphs and intricate behavior plans, hoping to impress families with how smart he was. Gary, much more experienced, took a wiser approach.

Gary connected with families before presenting data and intricate behavioral plans. For example, he figured most parents or caregivers were rushing to clean the house before "the new director" arrived. When he entered a home for the first time, Gary said things like, "Boy, I wish my house was this clean." Family members usually laughed and said, "Really? It's not messy?"

"You should see my house," Gary said. "Seriously. I have three daughters and my wife's a nurse. My place looks like a war zone." Families smiled. Gary seemed like a real person.

After light banter, Gary discussed the program book with parents and technicians. When families talked, he gave them his full attention. Then, he repeated some of their words back to them to show he was listening.

Gary used statements like, "It sounds like you have a busy work life and your son is a real handful when you get home." Parents nodded in strong agreement, saying, "Yes, that's exactly it. That's why getting the TV watching under control is so important." Gary used empathy statements so the families knew he understood their situations.

Why do you think families liked Gary? He was a real person to them. Like starting with a new client, Gary took time to build rapport. He used the same approach with other professionals, too. People liked Gary because he was a great communicator.

Your supervisor will tell you what communication guidelines apply to your specific company. Practice with your supervisor to know what personal information is okay or not okay to share. How do you think you could be a stronger communicator?

Describe/ discuss this item.

Write more examples.

F – 03 EXPLAIN HOW TO COMMUNICATE WITH STAKEHOLDERS (E.G., FAMILY, CAREGIVERS, OTHER PROFESSIONALS) AS AUTHORIZED.

(Supervisor only)

<u>Criteria</u>: *Interview*

<u>Assessment:</u>
- Ask technician to identify two examples and non-examples of what personal information is safe to share at work.
- Ask technician to state two ways to communicate effectively with one specific family member of caregiver on her or his caseload.
- Ask technician to identify a situation where she or he needed effective communication skills with other professionals recently.

Notes:

Assessment notes:

Notes:

Segment 10 – Scorecard
Ethics and Professional
Conduct

(Supervisor checks boxes)

☐ Individual Supervision
☐ Group Supervision

E 4
☐ Assessment
☐ Workbook boxes completed

F 4
☐ Assessment
☐ Workbook boxes completed

E 5
☐ Assessment
☐ Workbook boxes completed

F 5
☐ Assessment
☐ Workbook boxes completed

Segment 10 – Individual Supervision Agenda

Supervisor: _____ **Technician:** _____

Meeting Date: _____ **Time of meeting – From:** _____ **To:** _____

This document covers supervisory period from ____/____/____ **to** ____/____/____

1. Review Workbook Boxes:

    Has supervisee satisfactorily completed workbook boxes?   Yes / No

- If not, what is needed to complete boxes? Describe below

2. Task List items addressed (E 4-5; F 4-5)

3. Describe/Discuss task list items with technician

4. Discussion topics or activities completed during this meeting:

Evaluation of Technician's Performance				
(Record: S- "Satisfactory"; NI- "Needs Improvement"; U- "Unsatisfactory"; or NA- "Not Applicable")				
Arrived on time for meeting		Gave examples as needed		
Completed workbook boxes		Accepted supervisory feedback appropriately		
Referred to task list item		Answered all questions thoroughly		
Maintained professional communication during supervision meeting				
Overall evaluation of supervisee performance during this meeting *(Circle one—use code above)*			S NI U	
If "NI" or "U", please list corrective steps needed to achieve a score of "S"				

5. Practice assigned for next meeting

6. Closing questions/feedback

Segment 10 – Group Supervision Meeting Agenda

- <u>Meeting Topic</u>: Ethics and Professional Conduct

- <u>Task List Items Reviewed</u>:
- E-04 Describe applicable legal, regulatory and workplace reporting requirements (e.g., mandatory abuse and neglect reporting).
- E-05 Describe applicable legal, regulatory, and workplace requirements for data collection, storage, and transportation.
- F-04 Identify methods to maintain professional boundaries (e.g., avoid dual relationships, conflicts of interest, social media contracts).
- F-05 Identify methods to maintain client dignity.

1. Housekeeping
   - Take attendance.
   - State the duration of today's meeting.
2. Task List Lesson and Discussion
   - Discuss task list item E-04 Describe applicable legal, regulatory and workplace reporting requirements (e.g., mandatory abuse and neglect reporting).
   - Discuss task list item E-05 Describe applicable legal, regulatory, and workplace requirements for data collection, storage, and transportation.
   - Discuss task list item F-04 Identify methods to maintain professional boundaries (e.g., avoid dual relationships, conflicts of interest, social media contracts).
   - Discuss task list item F-05 Identify methods to maintain client dignity.
3. Segment Review
   - Review segment items from current meeting
   - Review workbook boxes from RBTs to generate discussion
   - When presenting material, use response cards and ask frequent questions (raise hand, write on a paper and hold up the answer, etc.)
   - Use behavioral skills training to keep information interactive.
   - Include role play at every group meeting and do not rely on lecture for the bulk of meeting.
   - Raise specific case examples. Provide enough context for others in group to understand the idiosyncrasies of case. Do not dominate the time by discussing one or a handful of clients. Cover enough material to engage all learners and evoke behavior from RBTs.
4. Questions
   - Answer any relevant questions.
   - If RBTs do not ask have questions, quiz them on what you have covered in the meeting.
5. Closing Notes
   - Reinforce writing in workbook boxes and preparation for assessment.
   - Close the meeting by inviting supervisees to request topics to be covered in upcoming meetings.

E – 04 DESCRIBE APPLICABLE LEGAL, REGULATORY AND WORKPLACE RE-PORTING REQUIREMENTS (E.G., MAN-DATORY ABUSE AND NEGLECT REPORT-ING).

What is it?

RBTs are required to comply with specific laws for abuse and neglect. In 2012, the National Survey on Abuse of People with Disabilities surveyed 7,289 people in the United States of America. Most of those respondents either had a disability (20.2%) or had an immediate family member with a disability (47.4%) (Baladerian, 2012).

- People with disabilities reported various forms of abuse (87.2% verbal-emotional abuse, 50.6% physical, 41.6% sexual, 37.3% neglect, and 31.5% financial).
- More than 90% of people with disabilities who were abused said the abuse occurred on multiple occasions.

Abuse is a serious topic. You may be the only witness. Speak with your supervisor or human resources professional what the policies are at your workplace and write notes in the space below.

For more information about the National Survey on Abuse of People Disabilities:
http://disability-abuse.com/survey/survey-re-port.pdf

Notes:

Describe/ discuss this item.

Write more examples.

E – 04 DESCRIBE APPLICABLE LEGAL, REGULATORY AND WORKPLACE RE-PORTING REQUIREMENTS (E.G., MAN-DATORY ABUSE AND NEGLECT REPORT-ING).

(Supervisor only)

Criteria: *Interview*

Assessment:

- Ask technician to write and describe the procedure for mandatory abuse and ne-glect reporting at her or his workplace.
- Recommended: Verify the information with a human resources professional at the RBT's company, regardless of whether you are an outside contractor or employee at the same organization.

Notes:

Assessment notes:

Notes:

E – 05 DESCRIBE APPLICABLE LEGAL, REGULATORY, AND WORKPLACE RE-QUIREMENTS FOR DATA COLLECTION, STORAGE, AND TRANSPORTATION.

What is it?

RBTs work with sensitive information. The behavioral service provider – which could be a school, center, agency, or something else – must comply with local laws, regulations, and policies for data collection, storage, and transportation.

Ask your supervisor or human resources professional what the policies are at your workplace and write notes in the space below.

Notes:

Describe/ discuss this item.

Write more examples.

E – 05 DESCRIBE APPLICABLE LEGAL, REGULATORY, AND WORKPLACE REQUIREMENTS FOR DATA COLLECTION, STORAGE, AND TRANSPORTATION.

(Supervisor only)

<u>Criteria</u>: *Interview*

<u>Assessment:</u>

- Ask technician to identify specific requirements for data collection.
- Ask technician to identify specific requirements for data storage.
- Ask technician to identify specific requirements for data transportation.

Notes:

Assessment notes:

Notes:

F – 04 IDENTIFY METHODS TO MAINTAIN PROFESSIONAL BOUNDARIES (E.G., AVOID DUAL RELATIONSHIPS, CONFLICTS OF INTEREST, SOCIAL MEDIA CONTACTS).

What is it?

It is not enough to say, "Have professional boundaries." Sometimes it is unclear where to draw the line. This task list item helps you identify ways to maintain boundaries at work to keep you out of trouble with your company and the BACB®.

Why does this matter?

RBTs must follow guidelines outlined in the BACB® Compliance Code, including professional boundaries and multiple (dual) relationships. You could lose your job, be removed from a client, or face sanctions on your RBT™ credential for problems with professional boundaries.

Example:

The client's mother arrives late to session. She says, "Jacinda, I'm so sorry. I'm 15 minutes late. It's my fault, not yours. I don't want you to be punished by having to stay 15 more minutes at the end. I'll just sign your timesheet for the regular time and you can still leave at 4:00 pm." Jacinda, an RBT™, has seen this situation before. She knows that little favors and secrets lead to problems. She remembered her behavioral skills training seminar last weekend at the TrainABA, "Ethical Gray-area Events" workshop. She started with an empathy statement, then stated the problem, a rationale, and then a solution. She said, "Mrs. Corning, I know traffic was a mess today and you were thinking of me by offering to sign the timesheet a few minutes early. With the company policy and BACB® Compliance Code, I won't be able to do that. I can stay until 4:15 pm, but if you need to leave we can just mark the timesheet from when you arrived and end at 4:00 pm." Mrs. Corning said, "Oh, I did not realize that. Okay, that makes sense about your policies. I understand. We can stay until 4:15 pm. I'm so sorry about this." Jacinda said, "Thank you, Mrs. Corning. Okay, 4:15 pm it is." Jacinda handled that situation well.

Example 2:

A few days later, Jacinda arrived at a different client's house and conducted a two-hour session. At the end, the client's extended family had assembled in the living room with a specially wrapped gift. The client's mother handed the gift to the client and helped him walk toward her. All the family members cheered. One uncle was recording video of this on his cell phone. "Give the gift to Jacinda," the mother told her son. Everyone was smiling, cheering, and clapping for Antonius, the client, to give Jacinda the gift. Jacinda knew she was not supposed to accept gifts. What should Jacinda have done?

Jacinda knew that she was supposed to refuse gifts in the moment using an empathy statement, stating the problem and rationale, and perhaps closing on the empathy statement again. Yet the rule was different for group situations. Jacinda knew she was supposed to accept the gift initially to be polite. The family insisted that she open the wrapping paper, which she did. It was a set of beauty products. Jacinda loved that brand of lipstick but she did not open it or use it. She needed to give it back soon.

Jacinda called Antonius' mother on the phone privately. "I'm not on speakerphone, am I?" said Jacinda. "No, it's just me," said the client's mother, "What's up?"

Jacinda said, "It was sweet of you to give me a gift and so fun for Antonius to give me a present in front of the whole family. That was thoughtful. With my company policy and RBT™ credential guidelines, I am not allowed to accept gifts so I have to give it back to you but thank you for the very nice gesture."

Antonius' mother said, "Oh, I did not know that. Well, that makes sense and how good of you to follow the rules. This is one more reason why I appreciate you – you play by the rules. Feel free to bring it by tomorrow at session. Thanks for saying it over the phone instead of in front of my whole family. It would have been weird if you declined the gift at the time, plus Antonius would have been confused and we are trying to get him ready for the holidays coming up."

Jacinda was glad she handled the situation professionally. She made the right choice.

Describe/ discuss this item.

Write more examples.

F – 04 IDENTIFY METHODS TO MAINTAIN PROFESSIONAL BOUNDARIES (E.G., AVOID DUAL RELATIONSHIPS, CONFLICTS OF INTEREST, SOCIAL MEDIA CONTACTS).

(Supervisor only)

Criteria: *Interview*

Assessment:

- Ask technician what social media platforms she or he uses and what can be done to maintain professional boundaries on such networks.
- Ask technician to identify a potential multiple relationship within her or his caseload or professional network and how to maintain professional boundaries.
- Ask technician to role play what to say if a family member or caregiver offered her or him a gift at the end of a session.*
- Ask technician the above question for a scenario where a whole group of family members were present when the gift was presented (i.e., aunts, uncles, parents, and neighbors prompt the client to present gift to you). *
- Ask about the above scenario for edible gifts, such as the family offering to give an extra plate of food to the technician while the child eats dinner during session. *

*See BACB® Newsletter, May 2015 for more information on gift giving or take Ben Theisen's Ethics for Supervision continuing education workshop at http://trainaba.com.

Notes:

Assessment notes:

Notes:

F – 05 IDENTIFY METHODS TO MAINTAIN CLIENT DIGNITY.

What is it?

Freedom from punishment, demands and restrictions is not enough. As a science, applied behavior analysis aims to dignify clients by empowering them with more skills and ways to access things they like. The goal is to help clients become independent.

Example:

Jim, a new RBT™ in Los Angeles, California, began working with two new clients. Roger, his first client, was a 17-year-old boy with intellectual disability. Lachelle, his other client, was a 5-year-old girl with autism. Jim observed sessions with the previous technicians for both clients. He noticed something interesting. When Roger asked for a break at sessions, the RBT™ gave him time without demands. After 5-minute timer, Roger would turn off the beeping sound and resume the task. When Jim observed Lachelle's sessions, he noticed she asked for a break and pointed to the large teddy bear she often cuddled. The technician said, "No break. We're working," and used hand-over-hand prompts to keep Lachelle on task with block imitation. Jim wondered why Lachelle was not allowed to have a break.

Jim observed Lachelle tantruming. She pointed to the teddy bear and cried, screaming, "Teddy!" Lachelle ran away from the technician, grabbing the teddy bear. The technician pried the teddy bear from Lachelle's hands and carried her – despite her kicking and screaming – back to the tabletop to finish the block imitation program with hand-over-hand prompts. Jim thought about it. He could never have done that with Roger, who was too large at 17 years old. Was it okay to move Lachelle like that? Or to refuse to give her breaks?

Jim remembered learning about reinforcement during training. Reinforcement makes behavior more likely to happen again. Sometimes it came from avoiding something unpleasant. Other times the reinforcement was something extra, pleasant, desired, and fun. Jim tried to think of an example of different kinds of reinforcers. He suspected that not all reinforcement was the same.

The best example Jim could think about was when he was bullied in elementary school. One bully pinned him to the ground and would not let him up until he said gave him his lunch money. The next time Jim saw the bully, he got the money ready because he figured he would rather give up money than get pinned down again. Jim realized that learning occurred – he gave money to the bully the next day – but he hated the bully. Jim did not want to learn anything else the bully could teach him. Was that the best way for Lachelle to view Jim? What about Roger? Jim was a skinny vegan from Silver Lake in Los Angeles, California. He played guitar in an indie rock band on the weekends. He viewed himself as a lover, not a fighter. He did not want his clients to despise him. Besides, Roger could easily overpower him. Jim thought carefully.

He decided to call his supervisor and ask if he could focus more on positive reinforcement with Lachelle and Roger. "I'm not worried about Roger's program," Jim told his supervisor, "because he has that break card thing going on." The supervisor said, "That's right, Jim. We could use a break card with Lachelle, too. I can send you a write-up of her program in the morning. Take a look at your email and let me know if you are comfortable implementing the plan." "Why, that's great," Jim said, "I think we're onto something."

Jim implemented the break card with Lachelle and it helped almost immediately. She overused it in the first session but Jim kept her favorite teddy bear at the work table and gave it to her for work completed, not the breaks she requested. Lachelle was successful during sessions with Jim.

Jim went on to recognize many ways to maintain client dignity during future sessions with new clients. He made a list of a few things that worked:

- Letting Roger open his own juice box instead of doing it for him
- Not mentioning his client's diagnosis to people who did not absolutely need to know
- Not talking to Roger's mother in the kitchen when the Roger was listening in the living room nearby.
- Not sharing personal details about a client to others (ABA was a small community)
- Introducing himself to peers as, "Jim," not, "Jim, the behavior analyst that is here to help with a functional assessment"

Client dignity is a big issue. Think about your clients now. What are you doing currently to dignify them? What possible changes might you suggest to your supervisor?

Describe/ discuss this item.

Write more examples.

F – 05 IDENTIFY METHODS TO MAINTAIN CLIENT DIGNITY.

(Supervisor only)

<u>Criteria</u>: *Interview*

<u>Assessment:</u>

- Ask technician to identify some general methods to maintain client dignity.
- Mention a specific client on the technician's caseload. How does the behavioral program maintain client dignity?
- Ask RBT™ to think of a specific client. What could be done differently to better preserve that client's dignity?

Notes:

Assessment notes:

Notes:

Segment 11 – Scorecard Assessment

(Supervisor checks boxes)

☐ Individual Supervision
☐ Group Supervision

B 2
☐ Assessment
☐ Workbook boxes completed

B 3
☐ Assessment
☐ Workbook boxes completed

B 4
☐ Assessment
☐ Workbook boxes completed

Segment 11 – Individual Supervision Agenda

Supervisor: _____ **Technician:** _____

Meeting Date: _____ **Time of meeting – From:** _____ **To:** _____

This document covers supervisory period from ____/____/____ to ____/____/____

1. Review Workbook Boxes:

　　Has supervisee satisfactorily completed workbook boxes?　　Yes / No

- If not, what is needed to complete boxes? Describe below

2. Task List items addressed (B 2-4)

| |
| |

3. Describe/Discuss task list items with technician

| |
| |

4. Discussion topics or activities completed during this meeting:

Evaluation of Technician's Performance				
(Record: S- "Satisfactory"; NI- "Needs Improvement"; U- "Unsatisfactory"; or NA- "Not Applicable")				
Arrived on time for meeting		Gave examples as needed		
Completed workbook boxes		Accepted supervisory feedback appropriately		
Referred to task list item		Answered all questions thoroughly		
Maintained professional communication during supervision meeting				
Overall evaluation of supervisee performance during this meeting *(Circle one—use code above)*		S	NI	U
If "NI" or "U", please list corrective steps needed to achieve a score of "S"				

5. Practice assigned for next meeting

| |
| |

6. Closing questions/feedback

| |
| |

Segment 11 – Group Supervision Meeting Agenda

- <u>Meeting Topic</u>: Assessment

- <u>Task List Items Reviewed</u>:
- B-02 Conduct preference assessments.
- B-03 Describe how you would assist with individualized assessment procedures (e.g., curriculum-based, developmental, social skills).
- B-04 Assist with functional assessment procedures.

1. Housekeeping
   - Take attendance.
   - State the duration of today's meeting.
2. Task List Lesson and Discussion
   - Discuss task list item B-02 Conduct preference assessments.
   - Discuss task list item B-03 Describe how you would assist with individualized assessment procedures (e.g., curriculum-based, developmental, social skills).
   - Discuss task list item B-04 Assist with functional assessment procedures.
3. Segment Review
   - Review segment items from current meeting
   - Review workbook boxes from RBTs to generate discussion
   - When presenting material, use response cards and ask frequent questions (raise hand, write on a paper and hold up the answer, etc.)
   - Use behavioral skills training to keep information interactive.
   - Include role play at every group meeting and do not rely on lecture for the bulk of meeting.
   - Raise specific case examples. Provide enough context for others in group to understand the idiosyncrasies of case. Do not dominate the time by discussing one or a handful of clients. Cover enough material to engage all learners and evoke behavior from RBTs.
4. Questions
   - Answer any relevant questions.
   - If RBTs do not ask have questions, quiz them on what you have covered in the meeting.
5. Closing Notes
   - Reinforce writing in workbook boxes and preparation for assessment.
   - Close the meeting by inviting supervisees to request topics to be covered in upcoming meetings.

B – 02 CONDUCT PREFERENCE ASSESS-MENTS.

Definition:
Preference assessment – an assessment to iden-
    tify high preference items to be used as rein-
    forcers in behavioral programming

Why is this important?
Identifying high preference items is an important
part of being an RBT. It is the responsibility of the
RBT to find items and activities that can be used
to reinforce behavior we want to see with our clients. If we do not have positive reinforcers identified, we often will see problematic behavior occur
when we place demands on clients. We also want
to make sure that our clients are happy when we
walk through the door.

There are several types of preference assessments
we can choose from to identify high preference
items. Each BCBA may have a favorite assessment
to use. She will provide you with specific training
on how to run them.

Here are a few you should know about:
- Multiple stimulus without replacement-
  MSWO (DeLeon & Iwata, 1996)
- Paired stimulus (Fisher et al., 1992)
- Response restriction (Hanley et al., 2003)

If you plan on running a preference assessment,
    you will need to identify 8-10 items that can
    be used in the assessment. You'll want to
    get a caregiver report of items they say may
    be highly preferred. It may also be good to
    put in a few items the participant has not
    used before.

When putting items in the assessment, separate
    food and toy items into different analyses.
    Run one assessment for food items and an-
    other for toy items.

Describe/discuss this item.

Write more examples.

B – 02 CONDUCT PREFERENCE ASSESSMENTS.

(Supervisor only)

<u>Criteria</u>: *Role play*

<u>Assessment</u>:
- Role play an MSWO. Have items and a datasheet ready for the technician to use.
- Role play 10-15 trials of a paired stimulus preference assessment. Have items and a datasheet ready for the technician to use.

Notes:

Assessment notes:

NOTES:

B – 03 DESCRIBE HOW YOU WOULD ASSIST WITH INDIVIDUALIZED ASSESSMENT PROCEDURES (E.G., CURRICULUM-BASED, DEVELOPMENTAL, SOCIAL SKILLS.)

<u>Why is this important?</u>

Assessment procedures are an important part of developing a good behavior program. As an RBT you could be asked to help out in running baseline trials for skill assessment, collecting data, answering interview questions or possibly even conducting a parent interview yourself.

Many assessment procedures are designed for professionals with a master's degree but there are some assessments that your BCBA supervisor would ask your help with.

Some assessments that may require your assistance may be:

- Skill based assessments – running baseline trials to identify skills the client currently has. These assessments may identify skills related to academics, social skills, or daily living skills

- Preference assessment – the BCBA supervisor may have you run some preference assessments to identify high preference items to be used as reinforcers in the behavior plan

- Interview – the BCBA supervisor may interview you for an assessment because you are a caretaker that may spend many hours with the client each week

- Caretaker interview – the BCBA supervisor may ask you to get some information from the parent/caretaker to inform an assessment

Describe/discuss this item.

Write more examples.

B – 03 DESCRIBE HOW YOU WOULD AS-
SIST WITH INDIVIDUALIZED ASSESS-
MENT PROCEDURES (E.G., CURRICULUM-
BASED,   DEVELOPMENTAL,   SOCIAL
SKILLS.)

(Supervisor only)

Criteria: *Interview*

Assessment:
- Based on the information that has been
  given to the technician about how RBTs
  may help assist with assessment procedures at your workplace, ask the technician to describe the responsibility she
  may have with assisting with those assessments.

Notes:

Assessment notes:

Notes:

B – 04 ASSIST WITH FUNCTIONAL ASSESS-MENT PROCEDURES

Why is this important?

Functional assessment procedures are designed to help BCBA supervisors understand more about what may be going on in the natural environment that is contributing to problematic behavior.

Because those BCBAs are not with the client as much as an RBT is, it can be helpful to the BCBA to get assistance from the RBT to get information. Just like the procedures described in B-03, there are specific tasks that the RBT is competent to accomplish. The BCBA supervisor may ask you to:

- Collect data
    - ABC narrative – This is a description of the "**A**ntecedents" "**B**ehavior" & "**C**onsequences" each time a problem behavior occurs.
    - Continuous measures
        - Frequency
        - Duration
    - Discontinuous measures
        - Partial interval
        - Whole interval
        - Momentary time sample
- Answering interview questions
    - You likely spend a good amount of time with the client. This is an advantage for the BCBA, who doesn't get the opportunity. Your experience and information is valuable.
- Conduct caretaker interviews
    - Get information about the context in which problem behavior is occurring from caretakers.

Describe/discuss this item.

Write more examples.

B – 04 ASSIST WITH FUNCTIONAL ASSESS-MENT PROCEDURES

(Supervisor only)

<u>Criteria</u>: *Role play*

<u>Assessment</u>:
- Roleplay assessment procedures that may be valuable to you and/or BCBAs at your workplace.
- Ask the technician to collect ABC data on a role play episode you create. Provide technician with a datasheet.

REMEMBER: For this part of the assessment, the technician can be assessed by having the candidate collect ABC data. Further evaluation of the skill may be accomplished via interview.

Notes:

Assessment notes:

Notes:

Segment 12 – Scorecard
Data Entry

(Supervisor checks boxes)

☐ Individual Supervision
☐ Group Supervision
☐ <u>RBT™ Renewal Application</u>

A 5
☐ Assessment
☐ Workbook boxes completed

Segment 12 – Individual Supervision Agenda

Supervisor: _____ **Technician:** _____

Meeting Date: _____ **Time of meeting – From:**_____ **To:**_____

This document covers supervisory period from ____/____/____ **to** ____/____/____

1. Review Workbook Boxes:

   Has supervisee satisfactorily completed workbook boxes?   Yes / No

- If not, what is needed to complete boxes? Describe below

2. Task List items addressed (A 5)

3. Describe/Discuss task list items with technician

4. Discussion topics or activities completed during this meeting:

Evaluation of Technician's Performance				
(Record: S- "Satisfactory"; NI- "Needs Improvement"; U- "Unsatisfactory"; or NA- "Not Applicable")				
Arrived on time for meeting		Gave examples as needed		
Completed workbook boxes		Accepted supervisory feedback appropriately		
Referred to task list item		Answered all questions thoroughly		
Maintained professional communication during supervision meeting				
Overall evaluation of supervisee performance during this meeting *(Circle one—use code above)*			S NI U	
If "NI" or "U", please list corrective steps needed to achieve a score of "S"				

5. Practice assigned for next meeting

6. Closing questions/feedback

Segment 12 – Group Supervision Meeting Agenda

- <u>Meeting Topic</u>: Data Entry

- <u>Task List Items Reviewed</u>:
- A-05 Enter data and update graphs.

1. Housekeeping
   - Take attendance.
   - State the duration of today's meeting.
2. Task List Lesson and Discussion
   - Discuss task list item A-05 Enter data and update graphs.
3. Segment Review
   - Review segment items from current meeting
   - Review workbook boxes from RBTs to generate discussion
   - When presenting material, use response cards and ask frequent questions (raise hand, write on a paper and hold up the answer, etc.)
   - Use behavioral skills training to keep information interactive.
   - Include role play at every group meeting and do not rely on lecture for the bulk of meeting.
   - Raise specific case examples. Provide enough context for others in group to understand the idiosyncrasies of case. Do not spend too much time discussing one or a handful of clients. Cover enough material to engage all learners and evoke behavior from RBTs.
4. Questions
   - Answer any relevant questions.
   - If RBTs do not ask have questions, quiz them on what you have covered in the meeting.
5. Closing Notes
   - Reinforce writing in workbook boxes and preparation for assessment.
   - Close the meeting by inviting supervisees to request topics to be covered in upcoming meetings.

- ## Remind RBTs to prepare renewal application. Use TRACK to complete renewal.

   - Congratulate RBTs for completing the 12th month of supervision curriculum. Hooray! Now ditch work and go celebrate. (Wait, that's not ethical. Say, "Nice work," and give a two-second handshake instead.) As for us, we'll see you again at Segment 1 next month.

A – 05 ENTER DATA AND UPDATE GRAPHS.

<u>Why is this important?</u>
Entering data and updating graphs is a responsibility that is often given to RBTs. This allows the BCBA to make data-based decisions about behavioral programming. Data and graphing are what set ABA apart from other interventions used to treat behavioral problems. Making decisions based on the data we collect is what makes ABA a science of behavior.

Primarily, we enter three types of data:
- Assessment data – baseline
- Discrete trial (DTT) or natural environment training (NET) data
- Problem behavior data

Different workplaces use different graphing programs. Some use paper graphs, others use computer programs like Microsoft Excel. More and more software programs for data collection are moving to cloud-based programs and apps on tablets or mobile devices. Such applications often update graphs automatically.

Your supervisor will provide extra training needed to use the software you are expected to use at your workplace.

Describe/ discuss this item.

Write more examples.

A – 05 ENTER DATA AND UPDATE GRAPHS.

(Supervisor only)

<u>Criteria</u>: *Role play*

<u>Assessment</u>:
- Ask technician to enter data into the software program used by your workplace.
- Ask technician to update the graphs for the software program used by your workplace.

REMEMBER: This is an entire segment designed to prepare your RBT to use the software and produce graphs that are useful for your behavioral programming. Extra training is required.

Notes:

Assessment notes:

Notes:

References

Baladerian, N., Coleman, T., & Stream, J. A report on the 2012 national survey on abuse of people with disabilities. Retrieved from http://disability-abuse.com/survey/survey-report.pdf

Cooper, J. O., Heron, T. E., & Heward, W. L. (2007). *Applied behavior analysis* (2nd ed). Upper Saddle River, N.J: Pearson/Merrill-Prentice Hall.

DeLeon, I. G., & Iwata, B. A. (1996). Evaluation of a multiple-stimulus presentation format for assessing reinforcer preferences. *Journal of Applied Behavior Analysis, 29*(4), 519–533.

Fisher, W. W., Piazza, C. C., & Roane, H. S. (2014). *Handbook of applied behavior analysis.* New York: Guilford Press.

Hanley, G. P., Iwata, B. A., Lindberg, J. S., & Conners, J. (2003). Response-restriction analysis: I. Assessment of activity preferences. *Journal of Applied Behavior Analysis, 36*(1), 47–58.

Johnston, J. M., & Pennypacker, H. S. (2009). *Strategies and Tactics of Behavioral Research* (3rd ed). New York: Routledge.

Malott, R. W., & Trojan, E. A. (2008). *Principles of behavior.* Pearson Prentice Hall Upper Saddle River.

Stokes, T. F., & Baer, D. M. (1977). An implicit technology of generalization. *Journal of Applied Behavior Analysis, 10*(2), 349.

Made in the USA
San Bernardino, CA
09 September 2018